Remember Me?

LOVING AND CARING FOR A DOG WITH CANINE COGNITIVE DYSFUNCTION

Eileen Anderson

Bright Friends Productions
Little Rock, Arkansas

Bright Friends Productions
1818 N. Taylor Street, Suite 8, #327
Little Rock, Arkansas 72207
www.brightfriendsproductions.com

Remember Me? Loving and Caring for a Dog with Canine Cognitive Dysfunction/ Eileen Anderson.—1st ed.
ISBN 978-1-943634-01-9

In Praise of *Remember Me?*

"Meticulously researched, accurate information presented with real empathy. I hope owners and trainers read this and get their dogs help sooner rather than later should they be afflicted." **—Jean Donaldson, author of *The Culture Clash*, founder of the Academy for Dog Trainers**

"Many families and all small-animal veterinarians will face the clinical signs of cognitive dysfunction eventually. And with the help of this book, they no longer have to deny its existence or pretend the clinical signs are the result of 'normal' aging. Eileen approaches this complex disease with a combination of scientific rigor and deep empathy for the animals and people who suffer from it. Her approach is clear, practical, open, and empathetic. Thank you, Eileen, for providing yet another excellent resource for animal lovers everywhere." **—E'Lise Christensen, DVM DACVB (board certified veterinary behaviorist)**

"While always conveying deep compassion and sensitivity for dogs with CCD, Eileen also recognizes the difficulties and stress that this disorder can place upon owners. ... In finishing this book, I realized that while Eileen had written it specifically to help senior dogs with CCD, the information found in its pages will also be of interest and help to all who live with senior dogs, as we strive to keep their lives happy, healthy, and enriched." **—Linda P. Case, author of *Beware the Straw Man* and owner of AutumnGold Consulting & Dog Training Center**

"Personal, easy to read, and full of useful information, Remember Me? is a must-have for everyone living with a dog. Once you have read this book, and I recommend you read it now, you'll want to keep it accessible as a reference for when you need it most." —**Lori Stevens, CPDT-KA, SAMP, owner, Seattle TTouch**

"What a marvelous book this is! I have been fortunate to have shared my life with a rather large number of beloved dogs. Having so far outlived all of them, I can only look back and wish I had had the common sense and wisdom available in this book to help me through the hardest times—the times when it was left to me to figure out how best to help my friends as they started to fade away, and, eventually, to decide if and when their need to go on superseded my desire to hold on tight.

With ample references, case studies, and personal stories, Eileen has fleshed out the many problems and joys of caring for an old dog. This book is an invaluable tool which will be in my 'toolbox' for many years to come!" —**Sue Ailsby, author of** *Training Levels: Steps to Success* **and instructor at Fenzi Dog Sports Academy**

Contents

Acknowledgements

Thank you to Cricket, my little dear one, for leading us on this journey together. To Summer, for turning my life in a new direction, towards dogs and training. To Zani, for helping me be less of a clod in the dog world. To Clara, for letting me raise her.

To Ruth Byrn and Gail Anderson, my wonderful family and dedicated first readers, a special thank-you for your belief in me and your patience with the project. To Kiki Yablon, the editor who partnered with me over this project with such skill and finesse that I am forever spoiled. (By the way, I made changes to the book after her last look at it. All mistakes are mine.) To Sue Matthews and Blanche Axton, for generously allowing me to reprint their down-to-earth writings about their dogs' last days. To Lisa Mantle, trainer extraordinaire, who always advocates for the dogs. To Marge Rogers, who said, in 2012: "You should have a blog."

To my generous reviewers: Sue Ailsby, Linda Case, E'lise Christensen, Jean Donaldson, and Lori Stevens, who took the time to read this book and give me feedback. To the online dog training community and the endless discussions where I learn so much. Yes really. Even from the fights. To my science and critical thinking buddies, who keep me honest. To my blog readers, who keep me writing.

My life is so enriched by all of you.

For Cricket, of course

Online Resources

This book contains references to online videos and blog posts that may be helpful to owners of senior dogs. Since web addresses are often unwieldy and sometimes change, they are not included.

Instead, I have created a companion document to this book that lives on the Internet. It has live links to all the resources mentioned, organized by chapter. You can find this document at *dogdementia.com/linklist.*

Introduction

Is your older dog starting to get stuck in corners, stare at walls, or act a little distant? Is he pacing in circles, barking for no apparent reason, or forgetting his housetraining? These or other behavioral changes may indicate that he has canine cognitive dysfunction, a disease akin to Alzheimer's. It's referred to informally as dog dementia.

My rat terrier, Cricket, had canine cognitive dysfunction for the last two years of her life. I had never heard of CCD before, nor seen a dog with the disease. I learned about it, and how best to help Cricket, as I went along. Watching a dog decline is heartbreaking, but that's not the focus of this book. Instead, I hope you'll find both comfort and practical help here, including ways to continue to provide your dog a rich and happy life for longer than you thought you could.

If the disease is in an early stage, there are drugs, supplements, dietary changes, and other measures that may help. CCD can't be cured, but its progression can be slowed in some dogs. If your dog has a fairly advanced case, I hope the tips about products and methods for keeping your dog safe will be helpful. Finally, if your dog is failing and you are struggling with the question of euthanasia, I hope the writings and resources here can help you make the best decision for you and your beloved companion.

I know the main audience for this book will be people with dogs already in cognitive decline, but I hope it will reach those with middle-aged and even young dogs as well. Some of the interventions that have been shown to slow cognitive decline work best if started early. In many cases, that's before the dog is showing any signs of CCD. No matter what decisions we make about how to treat it, I believe familiarity with CCD can help us keep our dogs happier and more comfortable from the time of their earliest symptoms.

Thank you for reading my book. May it help you have many more happy days with your dog.

[1]

Loving a Dog with Dementia: Cricket's Story

I first learned about canine cognitive dysfunction from my brave rat terrier, Cricket. This is our story.

Finding Cricket

Cricket was the first dog I ever chose myself.

My previous dogs and cats had all been off-the-street rescues. I hadn't gone looking for them, but they'd found me. At one time, I'd had four cats and three dogs. But in 2002, I was down to my senior rat terrier mix, Gabriel, and two cats, Andrew and Arabella. My house was nicely split in two with some French doors I'd installed when I moved in. I think my original idea was that I could have an area that was animal-free. Instead, the doors quickly became the divide between the cat area and the dog area. I did maintain one of my original goals of having a cat-free kitchen, but the dogs charmed their way in.

I had never trained any of my dogs, nor thought much about it. I had been fortunate that my animals had all been easygoing and gotten along with one another.

I wanted another dog. Specifically, I wanted another rat terrier, having fallen in love with Gabriel and two others I was acquainted with. Rat terriers seem to be my breed. Even to look at one makes me feel warm and happy. Their sharp lines and short coats, their bouncy movements, their musculature—they just look right to me. I'm sure anyone who loves a particular breed knows that feeling. I am partial to terriers in general, but rat terriers are the ones for me. I love that combination of tough and sweet.

So I knew what I wanted—but how to get it? Rescue websites were still fairly new then, and I'd never used one before, but I loved the idea immediately because I dreaded walking into a brick-and-mortar shelter. I found Ratbone Rescues online and "shopped" for a new dog to keep me and Gabriel company. Such a novel idea, that I could have a say in who came to live with us!

*Cricket looking more subdued
than she really was*

I was looking for a middle-aged female, hopefully somewhat sedate. Gabriel was full of personality but was slowing down a bit, and I didn't want to overwhelm him.

I kept going back to the profile for a little dog named Cricket who was being fostered about 500 miles from me. She was smaller than Gabe and looked very meek in her photo. She was said to be middle-aged. She had been abandoned by herself in an overnight box at a shelter. I still catch my breath when I think about that.

I applied to adopt her.

My friends teased me about the stringent process: extensive paperwork and a home visit. But I thought it was great. More power to the rescue for being so careful. Much harder, though, was convincing Cricket's foster family that I should have her. Although they had owned and fostered plenty of dogs, they were smitten with Cricket. They said she was the best foster they had ever had.

I had to write a series of persuasive emails, and actually talked to the head of the rescue, who told me to keep at it. Cricket's foster mom finally relented. She mentioned that she had relatives 150 miles from me whom she was going to visit at Christmas. She could bring Cricket along, then meet me partway between their home and mine.

We discussed Cricket's personality. Her foster mom said Cricket loved the other rat terrier in the home, was bossy with the Italian greyhounds, and let the Rhodesian ridgeback take her toys. (That seemed prudent to me.) We had quite a bit of discussion about whether she would likely get along with Gabriel, with the consensus being yes. (Nowadays I think this is funny, that we thought we could reason out whether two dogs would like each other.) Her foster mom mentioned that Cricket was sensitive about being touched around her neck and shoulders and even snapped sometimes when her collar was touched.

The Transfer

I was so excited. I had picked out a dog and now I was going to go get her. I drove the two hours by myself and met Cricket and her foster parents in a McDonald's parking lot. Cricket was very wired, dashing back and forth and repeatedly getting tangled up in her leash. They couldn't get her to go potty. I filled out more paperwork and wrote a check for her adoption fee. They tried urging her to get in my car on her own, and of course she wouldn't. Finally they picked her up and handed her to me, flailing. I put her in the car and closed the door. They left and got in their pickup, both of them fighting back tears.

Now I had a small whining, barking dog with me in the car. I had brought a crate in the backseat, but my preference was that she ride in front with me. (Remember, this was 2002.) She was frenetic, running from window to window, trying to look out. I just drove. After about 10 minutes of this, she came to me, snuggled up, and put her head in my lap. She stayed there without moving for the next two hours.

I picked up a friend on the way home. We took Cricket through the gate and into my backyard by herself. She had diarrhea almost immediately, and some of it clung to her rear end. She could clearly feel it, and waddled around looking at me. I fetched a tissue, and she let me wipe her butt. I guess you really have to be a dog person to understand this, but at that moment she became my dog.

My friend and I then spent the afternoon nailing sheets of plywood to the railings of my deck. Cricket was slender enough to slip through the balusters and jump down into the unfenced side yard, and she was also bold enough to try it.

At her first vet visit, the vet said she was in healthy middle age, probably six or seven years old.

Cricket and Gabriel

Cricket quickly started challenging Gabriel about all sorts of things. He outweighed her by at least four pounds, but they had heated arguments pretty regularly, which I allowed. (I wouldn't now.) Cricket usually came out on top. She was the only one to draw blood, and did so only once. Gabriel retained a little crescent-shaped scar over one eye for the rest of his life.

It turns out that Cricket, while basically friendly to other dogs, did whatever she could to monopolize access to her human. Other dogs were fine unless in competition for my attention. So poor, easygoing Gabriel kept getting the short end of the stick. He had slept under the covers with me for six years, but now Cricket very clearly told him no.

I regret this so much. Not that Gabriel hadn't had his day. He had bossed around my 70-pound shepherd mix for years and snapped at his face every day of their lives together. (I wouldn't allow that today either.) But I'm still sorry I didn't successfully intervene on his behalf when Cricket started hogging me.

Training

I took my extensive adoption agreement seriously. I felt I had to step up the quality of the life I was giving my dogs. Although I had never walked a dog regularly before, I felt that I owed it to Cricket, since I worked away from home on weekdays. So every day when I came home, I walked her up and down my little street. Then I came back and walked Gabriel separately.

Cricket pulled hard, all the time, on these walks. So I started to read up on training on the Internet.

I came across the "be a tree" method, where you simply stop forward motion every time the dog pulls. Readers, I did that for six months. Cricket continued to pull like a little freight train. She dug her front nails into the pavement so hard and so often that I never had to trim them. When I stopped, she then stood by my side looking around and barking frantically. Finally, she would loosen the leash by accident, and I would move forward a few steps, until she pulled the leash tight again. We spent much more time standing still than moving. Afterward, it was a relief to walk Gabriel, who pulled just a bit and whom I didn't try to train.

I didn't know enough about training then to understand why "be a tree" wasn't working with Cricket. I didn't know that I should have been reinforcing her behavior (for instance, with food) when she walked by my side. I didn't understand that we needed to practice in a less stimulating environment before trying the street. And I didn't know that I had picked one of the very hardest behaviors to train first. Instead, I concluded that Cricket wasn't very smart. I loved her to pieces, but boy, was she a dim bulb! She hadn't learned a thing in six months!

I finally got tired of providing entertainment for the neighbors, so I gave up and let Cricket pull me up and down the street. (The neighbors found this pretty entertaining too.)

Young Summer

I didn't try to train Cricket to do anything else for four years, until after Gabriel had died. By then I had taken in Summer, a young dog more than twice Cricket's size. When I started training her, in the hopes of addressing some behavior problems at home, Cricket demanded a turn. I used a handful of treats to teach her sit and down, as a lark, and was amazed at how fast she learned and how keen she was to do it. Forever after, when one dog had a training session, the other did too. You can't ignore that kind of joy.

I managed to learn enough about training to realize that Cricket had always been plenty smart. I had been the dim bulb.

I even took Cricket to some training classes, and she did great. We practiced for the Canine Good Citizen test, and she passed. I was so proud. I registered her with the American Kennel Club, and considered competing in rally obedience. She could do some really pretty heeling by then. But we didn't compete, mostly because I couldn't get her relaxed enough to lie down on cue in a competition ring.

Summer was going to doggie daycare during this time, and I started taking Cricket to work with me. I work in a quiet office, not open to the public, with one other woman. Cricket loved this.

We had a very full life: classes, the fun behaviors we practiced at home, walks every day, squirrels in the yard, and going to work together.

Three Dogs

In July 2009, I picked up a very friendly small hound mix I found running in the street. I thought she was about six months old, but the vet said she was more like a year. I put up signs and was contacted by the owner two days later. He asked if I wanted her. He was undergoing bankruptcy, and the dog was either crated 12 hours a day or left in his yard with a "holey" fence.

Young Zani, always up to something interesting

I snapped her up. This was Zani.

Zani became a new focus for my training efforts, along with Summer, but I continued training Cricket until her dementia got too advanced. A video I created entitled "Polite Pet Behaviors and Enrichment for a Senior Dog" shows some of the things I taught Cricket (see dogdementia.com/linklist).

With Zani in the picture, Summer and Cricket got excited more easily, and one day, when all the dogs were very worked up about some wildlife, Summer attacked Cricket, biting her repeatedly. It took Cricket several weeks to heal, and she had to wear a little coat in the hottest of summer weather so she wouldn't bother her stitches. I was emotionally devastated but decided to keep Summer. Forever after, Cricket and Summer were completely separated, even when I was at home with them. I used the French doors to divide the house. Zani, who got along with everybody, was allowed on either side.

What Are These Symptoms?

Tired after training class

In 2011, Cricket was probably 15 years old. I had been taking her to an occasional class at the dog training club, but stopped after it became too tiring for her. She was going deaf, and her vision was growing impaired.

However, she was still going to my office with me and really enjoying it. That's where I noticed the first sign of dementia, although I didn't identify it as such for a while.

Cricket had always loved my coworker, Ruth, who is also a dear friend of mine. But in 2011, she started avoiding her. If Ruth approached her, she turned away. She pulled back her head if Ruth tried to pet her or even offer her a treat. She looked scared.

I was perplexed. I knew it was unusual for a dog's behavior to change that much. I started watching Cricket more closely and observed that she seemed to be more anxious in other situations as well. She had always been what I would call high-strung, but now it seemed to be more than that. She trembled sometimes. She acted afraid of things she'd never feared before.

I wanted her to be able to be more relaxed. I knew that antianxiety medications were sometimes used for dogs, and I described Cricket's behavior changes to my vet. The vet prescribed fluoxetine (Prozac).

Cricket had a seizure after a week on the medication. I didn't know whether it was another symptom of what was going on with her or a side effect of the fluoxetine. I talked to the vet, and we agreed to stop the drug. The only other seizure she ever had was on the day she died.

So I felt sad about Cricket's anxiety, but I thought there was nothing I could do.

On our walks, another odd thing started happening. We generally walked on the left side of the street so she would be away from the traffic. Now, if I let her, she pulled left, into people's yards.

Since she was sniffing and not moving very quickly, I assumed she had merely gotten more interested in the yards. Our walks got shorter. She had some rear-end weakness, but wasn't really having any trouble with walking, so I couldn't understand why we weren't getting very far.

It was only later that I noticed she seemed to turn to the left a lot off-leash as well. She then started walking in counterclockwise circles, and finally sometimes slowly twirled in place. She had lost the ability to walk a straight line. You can see this in my video "Turning Circles: A Common Sign of Dementia in Dogs" (see dogdementia.com/linklist).

Waiting at the wrong side of the door

Next she began to misunderstand doors. I noticed this first at my office. Whenever I left for any reason, she waited right at the door. She continued that, but now half the time when I came back in she would be waiting at the hinge side of the door rather than where it opened. I attributed this to her deteriorating vision.

Also, she was starting to do things a forgetful human might. She would start to walk purposefully down the hall, get to the halfway point, and stop and just stand there.

I don't remember what made me finally investigate dementia. My mother had Alzheimer's disease, and I was learning about dementia in humans, so it could have been that. One day in the summer of 2011, I looked up "dementia in dogs" online.

I found a list of symptoms, almost all of which Cricket had. They included standing at the wrong side of the door, getting less friendly with known people, standing in corners, staring off into space, and more.

Cricket's Diagnosis

Diagnosis by a vet was straightforward, now that Cricket had all these symptoms and I knew to report them. The vet said she knew of cases that had developed very quickly and some that had developed slowly. She was hopeful that since the changes I had been seeing were gradual, Cricket's case would progress slowly. I was leery of medication because of the experience with fluoxetine, so I passed on that at first. A few months later, a knowledgeable friend shared some good information about the dementia medications available, and I approached the vet about it. She put Cricket on Anipryl, a brand name for selegiline.

The medication seemed to help. (There's more information on selegiline and other treatment options in chapter 3.) Cricket seemed to become more aware of what was going on again, although she still didn't usually walk in a straight line. She stayed on Anipryl and lived two more years while still retaining some capabilities and memory.

I will share what I learned in that two-year journey later in this book. The next section will cover the symptoms of dementia and how it's diagnosed.

[2]

Does Your Dog Have Dementia?

What's Going On with My Dog?

Lots of people are completely unaware of dog dementia until their dog starts behaving oddly. I was.

Canine cognitive dysfunction is probably extremely underdiagnosed. According to a study that included a survey returned by almost a thousand owners of dogs aged eight or older, 14.2 percent of the dogs had signs of cognitive decline (Salvin et al. 2010, 280). But only 1.9 percent of the dogs had been diagnosed with CCD. The researchers theorized that owners lacked knowledge of the disorder and were reluctant to discuss behavioral problems with the vet. They also noted that the vets lacked a validated assessment tool for CCD—a gap they went on to fill (see information on the Canine Cognitive Dysfunction Rating Scale below).

Another study of 180 senior dogs found that 28 percent of those 11 to 12 years of age showed signs of at least one type or category of behavioral impairment linked to cognitive dysfunction, and 10 percent showed signs of at least two categories of impairment (Neilson et al. 2001, 1789).

What's more, owners may not seek diagnosis—even when symptoms have been pointed out by experts. In another study of 124 senior dogs, none of whom had been identified by the owners as having behavioral problems, 75 were identified as having signs of cognitive dysfunction. Their owners were notified and advised to consult with their veterinarians, but fewer than half did so (Osella et al. 2007, 34).

Neither ignorance of the condition nor inaction can go on indefinitely. Dementia worsens over time. We are accustomed to this in our own species, but it's true for dogs as well. A 2001 study found that dogs who showed symptoms of cognitive dysfunction were likely to show a greater severity of those symptoms and/or additional types of symptoms from six to 18 months later (Bain et al. 2001, 1694).

It's also worth noting here that there are other diseases and health conditions in dogs that can cause dementia that are not necessarily related to aging, including brain tumors, tick-borne diseases, and liver abnormalities. Yet other conditions, such as vestibular disease, do not involve dementia but can have similar symptoms. Some of these can be treated, so any sign of cognitive difficulties in your dog should prompt a visit to the vet.

Canine cognitive dysfunction isn't rare in older dogs, but there are interventions to alleviate it. One of my hopes in writing this book is to bring information to the general public so that dogs with dementia can be identified and helped sooner.

Canine Cognitive Dysfunction Defined

Canine cognitive dysfunction is a term for mental and behavioral decline associated with changes in the brains of aging dogs. In this book, I use the terms *canine cognitive dysfunction* and *dementia* interchangeably, although the latter is a more general term.

The condition is also sometimes referred to as cognitive dysfunction syndrome in both dogs and cats.

Several types of brain changes have been identified and found to correlate with behaviors that typically accompany cognitive decline.

Those associated with cognitive dysfunction in canines bear similarities to, but are not exactly the same as, those associated with Alzheimer's disease in humans. They are close enough, though, that dogs are used as a model to study early Alzheimer's (Cummings, Head, Ruehl, et al. 1996).

One of the brain changes that can occur as mammals age is the development of beta-amyloid plaques. These are largely insoluble accumulations of protein fragments that are normally broken down and dissolved in the brains of younger animals. The development of plaques in older animals impedes communication between cells in the brain, affecting memory and learning. Several studies have shown a strong correlation between the presence of beta-amyloid plaques and cognitive decline in dogs (Cummings, Head, Afagh, et al. 1996).

Other brain changes that appear to accompany both aging and cognitive decline in dogs include oxidation damage, decreased glucose metabolism, and a decrease in frontal lobe volume (Landsberg, Nichol, and Araujo 2012, 751, 761).

One change in humans that's associated with Alzheimer's, the development of neurofibrillary tangles, is usually not present in dogs. Researchers speculate that this is because dogs don't live long enough for the tangles to develop.

"Dogs do not progress to the full Alzheimer's changes and don't develop such irreversible or major changes like people do," says canine cognitive dysfunction expert Dr. Gary Landsberg, a veterinary behaviorist based in Ontario, Canada. "That's why they are used as models for early Alzheimer's changes and why therapeutics might be more effective in animals." (Landsberg et al. 2008, 2)

Symptoms

The types of problems associated with canine cognitive dysfunction are often represented clinically by the acronym DISHA. DISHA stands for:

Disorientation
Interactions with people and other pets that have changed
Sleep-wake alterations
House soiling
Activity-level alterations

However, DISHA does not cover the complete spectrum of possible changes, which also includes memory and learning deficits, appetite changes, and anxiety and depression (Landsberg, Nichol, and Araujo 2012, 754).

The following is a list of potential indicators of canine cognitive dysfunction that I've compiled from many sources. You'll see photos of a good many of these behaviors in this book, and links to videos at dogdementia.com/linklist.

- Forgetting housetraining
- Difficulty learning anything new
- Seeking attention less, or seeming withdrawn
- Acting frightened, shy, or avoidant of known people
- Sleeping more during the day and less at night
- Appearing lost or confused

- Pacing back and forth or circling in one direction

Circling

- Staring off into space or at walls

Standing and staring

- Walking into corners or other tight spaces and staying there

Standing in a corner

- Failing to remember routines, or starting them and getting only partway through
- Getting lost in familiar places
- Barking for no apparent reason and/or for long periods
- Not barking in situations where barking previously would have occurred
- Trembling for no apparent reason
- Falling off things

- Trouble eating or drinking (finding the bowls, aiming the mouth, keeping food in the mouth)

Difficulty eating

- Difficulty getting all the way into bed

Difficulty with bed

- Getting trapped under or behind furniture

Stuck under a drawer

- Sleeping more during the day and less at night
- Appearing lost or confused
- Waiting at the hinge side of the door to go out (see photo on page 12)
- Failing to get out of the way when you open a door
- Forgetting cues and trained behaviors
- Exhibiting motor difficulties like trouble backing up (if not caused by physical problems)
- Startling easily
- Losing enthusiasm for toys or cessation of play altogether

- Performing repetitive behaviors
- Loss of appetite
- Not responding to name
- Trouble with stairs
- Getting generally more fearful or anxious

My video, "What Canine Cognitive Dysfunction Can Look Like," shows many of the above behaviors as well (see dogdementia.com/linklist).

However, any of these symptoms could be caused by a different health issue. It takes careful observation and a good discussion with your vet to determine if your dog may have CCD. As a first step, the vet will likely rule out some other conditions (Landsberg, Nichol, and Araujo 2012, 754).

Getting a Diagnosis

There is currently no physical test for CCD. There are two diagnostic methods: clinical and neuropsychological.

Clinical Diagnosis

To make a clinical diagnosis, a veterinarian will gather information about the dog's behavior and compare it to a list of known symptoms. Owners play a crucial part in this process. The vet may be able to observe some concerning behaviors when examining the dog, but owners will need to describe what the dog does at home.

To be sure you give your vet as complete a picture as possible, start by making a list. Record the behaviors that concern you. Include even the subtlest changes you have noticed, any little quirks that may be developing. Many of the early behavior changes can easily go under the radar. They did for me. Your vet will want to know about all possible symptoms.

You can also use the printable symptom checklist I've made available on my website (see dogdementia.com/linklist).

Your vet is likely to ask how long the various symptoms have been present. This is often difficult to answer. We don't tend to notice those subtle early shifts, or even if we do, most of us have some distortion in our sense of time (Hammond 2012). Give it some thought before your appointment with the vet so you can provide the best possible information.

If you're prepared to go beyond a simple list, there are more complex diagnostic aids available. One of these stands above the rest: the Canine Cognitive Dysfunction Rating Scale. The CCDR was developed through a scientific study and has been found to be extremely accurate in distinguishing cognitive dysfunction from normal aging (Salvin et al. 2011).

To create the CCDR, researchers distributed surveys to the owners of 957 older dogs. The surveys included questions about 27 behaviors previously found to correlate with canine cognitive dysfunction. Through data analysis, 13 questions were chosen to comprise the final rating scale. When tested on another group of dogs, the CCDR was found to have 98.9 percent diagnostic accuracy.

You can use the CCDR to check the likelihood of your dog having CCD. Dr. Hannah Salvin has kindly permitted me to link to two formats of the CCDR (see dogdementia.com/linklist). There is an online survey version and a downloadable copy for printing. The CCDR results do not take the place of a diagnosis by a veterinarian, but may prompt you to make an appointment.

Neuropsychological Diagnosis

Although this diagnostic method is rare and not currently available to pet owners, it bears mentioning. A dog's cognitive capabilities can actually be tested in a lab, his speed of learning and remembering information measured and scored. The method, used in experiments regarding canine cognitive dysfunction, is similar to the cognitive testing done with humans when brain dysfunction is suspected. With humans, these tests are usually administered by a licensed psychologist working in tandem with a medical clinic.

So after a dog is diagnosed—what then? Chapter 3 describes treatments that may help.

References

Bain, Melissa J., Benjamin L. Hart, Kelly D. Cliff, and William W. Ruehl. 2001. "Predicting Behavioral Changes Associated with Age-Related Cognitive Impairment in Dogs." *Journal of the American Veterinary Medical Association* 218 (11): 1792-1795.

Cummings, Brian J., Elizabeth Head, Arman J. Afagh, Norton W. Milgram, and Carl W. Cotman. 1996. "β-Amyloid Accumulation Correlates with Cognitive Dysfunction in the Aged Canine." *Neurobiology of Learning and Memory* 66 (1): 11-23.

Cummings, Brian J., Elizabeth Head, William Ruehl, Norton W. Milgram, and Carl W. Cotman. 1996. "The Canine as an Animal Model of Human Aging and Dementia. " *Neurobiology of Aging* 17 (2): 259-268.

Hammond, Claudia. 2012. Time Warped: Unlocking the Mysteries of Time Perception. Edinburgh: Canongate.

Landsberg, Gary, Amanda Florsheim, Valerie Dramard, Teodoro Bottiglieri, and David Mischoulon. 2008. "S-adenosylmethionine (SAMe) and cognitive dysfunction in dogs (Sponsored by Virbac Animal Health): A Roundtable Discussion." DVM360.com. (See dogdementia.com/linklist.)

Landsberg, Gary M., Jeff Nichol, and Joseph A. Araujo. 2012. "Cognitive Dysfunction Syndrome: A Disease of Canine and Feline Brain Aging." Veterinary Clinics of North America: Small Animal Practice 42 (4): 749-768.

Neilson, Jacqueline C., Benjamin L. Hart, Kelly D. Cliff, and William W. Ruehl. 2001. "Prevalence of Behavioral Changes Associated with Age-Related Cognitive Impairment in Dogs." *Journal of the American Veterinary Medical Association* 218 (11): 1787-1791.

Osella, Maria Cristina, Giovanni Re, Rosangela Odore, Carlo Girardi, Paola Badino, Raffaella Barbero, and Luciana Bergamasco. 2007. "Canine Cognitive Dysfunction Syndrome: Prevalence, Clinical Signs and Treatment with a Neuroprotective Nutraceutical." *Applied Animal Behaviour Science* 105 (4): 297-310.

Salvin, Hannah E., Paul D. McGreevy, Perminder S. Sachdev, and Michael J. Valenzuela. 2010. "Under Diagnosis of Canine Cognitive Dysfunction: A Cross-Sectional Survey of Older Companion Dogs." *The Veterinary Journal* 184 (3): 277-281.

Salvin, Hannah E., Paul D. McGreevy, Perminder S. Sachdev, and Michael J. Valenzuela. 2011. "The Canine Cognitive Dysfunction Rating Scale (CCDR): A Data-Driven and Ecologically Relevant Assessment Tool." *The Veterinary Journal* 188 (3): 331-336.

[3]

Is There a Treatment?

I worked on this book for a little over two years, and even in that short time, the number of possible treatments for CCD grew. However, dementia still cannot be cured, and the treatments that appear to successfully slow its progress have small or moderate effects.

Because of this, and because the symptoms can be hard to quantify or track, cognitive dysfunction is the type of condition that's attractive to food and supplement companies. Most of us want to believe that these more "natural"-sounding remedies work, even in the absence of good evidence that they do.

There are numerous products on the market for senior dogs that claim to support brain health, many of which are not proven to help. In this chapter, I have included only descriptions of treatments and activities that may help lessen the symptoms and effects of dementia in dogs as evidenced by at least one peer reviewed study and that have been included in review articles by experts in the field.

The interventions include prescription drugs, specially formulated diets, activities, and supplements. Some of the evidence for them is preliminary, coming from pilot studies or studies without control groups. I have not critiqued the studies or ranked the effectiveness of these treatments. Testing of these products is still new, and fresh information is arriving all the time. Information on side effects is lacking in some cases, so there is some risk involved. So this chapter should be regarded not as medical advice, but as a starting point for discussion with your veterinarian.

A complete reversal of the symptoms of canine cognitive dysfunction is not going to happen with any of the interventions we know about today. There are no miracle cures. But the treatments listed in this chapter may be able to improve your dog's capabilities and slow the development of the condition.

Some of the following information is fairly technical, and is intended for those who want details of the chemistry and biology involved. That information can easily be skimmed over if you just want the bottom line: how likely is it that this item will help my dog?

Prescription Drugs

Several drugs have been tested for their effectiveness in treating canine cognitive dysfunction. What your vet might recommend depends in part on your location; different drugs have been studied and approved for use in different areas.

Selegiline

Selegiline is a prescription drug sold under the brand names Anipryl, L-deprenyl, Eldepryl, Emsam, and Zelapar. In the United States, it's sold for dogs as Anipryl.

Selegiline is a selective irreversible monoamine oxidase B (MAO-B) inhibitor. MAO-B is an enzyme that acts on the central nervous system. It performs several roles, among them degrading dopamine, the brain hormone involved with the reward system. MAO-B levels have been shown to increase with age in many animals, including both humans and dogs. Elevated levels of MAO-B correlate with the incidence of Parkinson's disease in humans and are associated with general cognitive decline.

Selegiline is thought to halt or slow cognitive decline by reducing levels of MAO-B.

There have been several clinical trials of selegiline with dogs, starting in 1993 (Milgram et al. 1993). It is approved in the United States for use in dogs to lessen the effects of aging on cognition.

One thing most of the studies showed is that the efficacy of the drug varied among the individual dogs. At the time of this writing, a reason for the difference in responsiveness to the treatment had not been identified.

A large study in 2001, in which 641 dogs started and 474 completed the regimen, showed promising results (Campbell, Trettien, and Kozan 2001). After 30 days of treatment, a significant percentage of the dogs showed improvement in the following symptoms:

Symptom	Percentage of Dogs Who Improved
Disorientation	78
Decreased interaction	76
Loss of house training	73.5
Changes in activity or sleep/wake cycle	62.5

The treatment continued, and after 30 more days, results were recorded again. In the dogs who had improved by day 30, further improvement was reported by day 60:

Symptom	Percentage of Dogs Who Improved Further
Disorientation	55.3
Decreased interaction	53.0
Loss of house training	35.5
Changes in activity or sleep/wake cycle	41.2

Only a small set (under 10 percent in all categories) of the dogs who had not shown improvement by day 30 showed improvement by day 60. In other words, if a dog was going to improve, that was almost always clear by the 30-day mark.

Diarrhea, vomiting, and lack of appetite were reported in under 5 percent of the dogs. Other possible adverse effects were reported during the time period, but generally found not to be attributable to the selegiline.

It was noted that 9 percent of the dogs died or were euthanized during the study. But no deaths were linked to the drug. Keep in mind that these were aged dogs with preexisting medical conditions.

Nicergoline, Propentofylline, and Adrafinil

Two drugs that enhance blood flow to and within the brain are prescribed outside the United States for canine cognitive decline. Nicergoline, used in the United Kingdom, enhances blood flow to the brain and is thought to enhance the transmission of neurons. Propentofylline, used in some European countries and Australia, is thought to increase blood flow by making the red blood cells more pliable and inhibiting platelet aggregation. It is sold as a veterinary medicine in Australia under the name Vivitonin. At the time of this writing, these drugs had not been extensively studied for effectiveness in treating dementia.

One study measured the increase in physical activity in dogs after courses of nicergoline, propentofylline, and a third drug, adrafinil (Siwak, Gruet, Woehrlé, Muggenburg, et al. 2000). Nicergoline and propentofylline did not correlate with any change in observed activity, but adrafinil did. Increased activity is only one of many possible measures of effectiveness of a treatment for canine cognitive dysfunction, but the dogs that got adrafinil were observed to be more active both in their cages and in open-field tests.

Adrafinil showed other possible helpful effects. It is an eugeroic, a drug that promotes wakefulness. It improved dogs' attempts to learn discrimination tasks (Milgram et al. 2000), and in another study was shown to cause increased locomotion without stereotypical activity (repetitive, compulsive behavior). However, the dosing may be difficult, and more studies are needed (Siwak, Gruet, Woehrlé, Schneider, et al. 2000).

Other drugs can address individual symptoms that often accompany cognitive decline, such as anxiety or sleeplessness. You can ask your vet about those as well.

Specially Formulated Diets

Two commercially available supplemented diets have been tested and found to ameliorate the effects of canine cognitive dysfunction.

Hill's Prescription Diet b/d Canine Healthy Aging

Hill's Prescription Diet b/d Canine Healthy Aging & Alertness, an antioxidant-fortified food available in the United States, has been clinically shown to improve dogs' cognition in laboratory tests (Milgram et al. 2002).

The Hill's study tested both young and old dogs. The young dogs and old dogs were each divided into two groups: control and dietary intervention. All dogs underwent some initial testing, in which young dogs performed significantly better on some cognitive tasks than the senior dogs. This indicated that these types of tasks might be a good measure of the effects of aging on the brain. Then the dogs in the intervention groups were put on the antioxidant-fortified food for six months, while the dogs in the control groups ate a nonfortified food.

After six months on the diets, all dogs were tested with four learning problems of increasing difficulty. The senior dogs on the fortified diet performed better at the tasks than those in the senior control group. There was no difference in the performance between the two groups of younger dogs. This strengthened the hypothesis that the food specifically helped slow age-related cognitive decline. However, since the study did not isolate the nutrient variables, we do not know exactly what in the diet was the most helpful.

Purina One SmartBlend Vibrant Maturity 7+ Formula

A more recent study has been performed to test a diet containing medium-chain triglycerides, or MCTs (Pan et al. 2010). MCTs are believed to help the body compensate for a decline in glucose metabolism in the brain. The food tested can be purchased in the United States as Purina One SmartBlend Vibrant Maturity 7+ Formula.

Aged beagles who ate this food for eight months scored significantly better on several types of cognitive tasks than did a control group. The authors noted that the largest difference in performance between the two groups was seen on the more difficult tasks. There were two tasks that didn't show a significant difference in performance between the two groups, but none on which the control group performed significantly better.

A caution: These studies assess the effects of professionally created foods. A do-it-yourself approach to combining ingredients and supplements is not advised. Some supplements can be toxic at certain levels, or interact with prescription drugs. The clinical results come from much more controlled situations than we commonly can create at home. It you want to try to prevent or slow cognitive dysfunction in your dog by adjusting her diet, I advise consulting a veterinary nutritionist. She may encourage you to switch your dog to one of the above foods. Or by the time you see her, there may be another food available. Or she may be able to help you improve your dog's diet with a combination of purchased products and home-prepared foods.

Everyone wants a diet solution. It is a very attractive idea that we can solve a problem simply by changing what we eat. The preliminary research regarding cognitive decline in dogs is that some diet changes can help somewhat. But the research doesn't guarantee a positive result.

Environmental Enrichment

Enriching our dogs' lives with activities and stimulation has many benefits, and it turns out that one of them may be a slight buffering effect against cognitive decline, particularly in combination with dietary changes.

In a two-year study, cognitive abilities in senior beagles were measured under four different conditions (Milgram et al. 2004).

Some were given the Hill's antioxidant-fortified food described in the previous section. Some had enrichment consisting of exercise, toys, and training. Some had both food and enrichment, and some had no interventions. Two groups of young dogs were also included: one on a control diet and one on the antioxidant-fortified diet.

As in the 2002 study, the senior dogs on the special diet showed a statistically significant improvement in cognition. The group provided with enrichment did also. But the group of aged dogs that showed the highest improvement was the one that had both enrichment and the special diet.

Enrichment included:

- Social interaction with other dogs. The dogs in the enrichment group were housed with kennel mates.
- Exercise. Exercise has been shown to correlate with good health, including brain health, in many species.
- Toys. Sets of toys were given to the dogs and rotated every week.
- Cognitive challenges. The dogs were given a relatively difficult behavior to learn involving discrimination: detecting the difference in characteristics of objects and communicating that to the handler through a trained behavior. The paper emphasizes this aspect of the enrichment, pointing to research on humans indicating one must "use it or lose it," i.e., exercise the brain.

The authors conclude, and show some evidence, that the cognitive challenges were the most important of the enrichment activities.

There appeared to be no cognitive differences between the young dogs on the control food and those on the fortified food.

Another three-year study showed enhanced performance at spatial problem solving in aged dogs who were given an antioxidant-enriched diet and environmental enrichment similar to that described above (Nippak et al. 2007). This diet was created in the lab and is not commercially available. The authors noted that the positive effects were more marked the longer the study went on. They also noted that they did not determine which of the antioxidants used in the diet, or which in combination, were responsible for the positive effects.

Enrichment activities are beneficial in the moment, even if they don't slow the cognitive decline. Any time you can spend with your dog doing activities that are fun and challenging at the right level for her current capabilities is time that you and your dog will treasure.

And for those of you with a younger dog, or with plans to get one, you can build cognitive challenges and enrichment into her life from the very beginning. Though it's not a sure preventative of CCD, there is evidence that early learning is beneficial to dogs' learning abilities later in life (Milgram et al. 2004, 762). Teach her tricks using positive reinforcement. Hide her meals and let her sniff them out, or let her eat them out of puzzle toys. Give her chances to problem solve. Check out the ideas in chapter 4 of this book under "Enrichment."

Supporting General Health and Fitness

One of the best things we can do to for our dogs' overall health is to control their weight, and this likely has beneficial effects on cognition (Landsberg 2005, 475; Kealy et al. 2002).

Supplements

There are several supplements that may reduce or delay the effects of CCD.

SAMe

S-Adenosyl methionine (SAMe) is an amino acid that has been studied in both dogs and cats as well as humans and appears to have a range of beneficial effects, including reduction of joint pain and inflammation and antidepressant qualities. It's available as a supplement under many brand names.

A 2007 study on 36 dogs older than eight years who had demonstrated signs of cognitive dysfunction showed that after two months of treatment with either the supplement or a placebo, the dogs taking the supplement showed a 57 percent increase in activity (versus 9 percent in the placebo group) and a 60 percent increase in "awareness" (versus 20 percent in the placebo group) (Rème et al. 2007). "Awareness" comprised several scored factors, including mental alertness, orientation, directed activity, and social interaction.

The purpose of a placebo in this type of study is to ensure the owners or observers don't know whether the dog has gotten the experimental treatment or not. This helps to prevent bias.

In a 2012 study of dogs and cats, 14 aged dogs were treated either with Novifit, a brand name of SAMe marketed for dogs, or a placebo (Araujo et al. 2012). After 15 days, the dogs were tested with two learning tasks and a memory task. In the two learning tasks, the dogs treated with Novifit did not show an increase in learning errors as time passed, while dogs treated with the placebo, and also aged dogs in previous studies, did. No improvement was shown on the memory task for the dogs treated with Novifit. The effects of Novifit were similar in the cat study. The conclusion of the study was that Novifit selectively enhanced some learning capabilities in the dogs and cats, but not memory.

Both of these studies had small numbers of subjects. We can expect some larger studies on SAMe in the future. If you are interested in treating your dog with SAMe, please consult your veterinarian.

Phosphatidylserine

Phosphatidylserine is a part of a membrane that is found in a broad range of cell types in plants and animals. It has been used in human patients with Alzheimer's, and is included in the supplements Senilife and Aktivait for dogs and cats. In an initial exploratory study, Senilife showed promise, correlating with improvement in symptoms of CCD in five categories of behavior for eight dogs who took it for 84 days (Osella et al. 2007).

Aktivait was also tested in 2007 (Heath, Barabas, and Craze 2007). This study of 44 dogs included a control group whose members were given a placebo. At the end of 56 days, the dogs given Aktivait showed improvement in disorientation, social interactions, and toileting behaviors compared to the control group.

Note that these two studies were also very small.

Apoaequorin

Apoaequorin is a calcium-buffering protein sourced from jellyfish. It's said to combat the neurotoxin methylphenyltetradropyridine, which is associated with Parkinson's disease and dementia in humans, and is a component of the dog supplement Neutricks. An initial study with 23 aged dogs that compared the effect of apoaequorin and a placebo indicated that those treated with apoaequorin showed improvement in performing learning and attention tasks, but not memory tasks (Milgram et al. 2015).

A second study with 24 aged dogs compared the effects of apoaequorin with selegiline, and the dogs treated with apoaequorin performed better than those treated with selegiline on learning and attention tasks (Milgram et al. 2015).

Other Supplements

Coconut oil is a source of medium-chain triglycerides, the key component in the Purina food that was tested and found to improve aspects of cognition in old dogs (Pan et al. 2010). It is sold as a supplement for dogs.

Omega-3 fatty acids are also popular supplements. They promote brain-cell health and are a component of the special antioxidant diet above (Milgram et al. 2002). They can be given as supplements.

As with prescription drugs, there are also supplements that have been shown to address specific problems that commonly accompany canine cognitive dysfunction, such as sleeplessness or anxiety. Two common supplements are melatonin and Zylkene, both sold under many labels.

Again, please check with your vet if you wish to treat your pet with supplements. The supplement industry is largely unregulated in the U.S., and all sorts of unproven products are advertised as effective. Your vet can protect your dog against possible adverse drug interactions, advise on brand names and dosages, and check the most current research. More than one study has shown that the quality of ingredients in supplements varies widely, and that some brands of supplements do not even contain the substance advertised.

No supplement will make your dog act or think like a youngster again. But some may yield small improvements, which are precious as our dogs grow older.

What If My Vet Won't Prescribe Anything?

First, she may have good reason. Ask her! But there are some vets who are just not comfortable prescribing drugs that affect the mind or emotions. If this is the case with your vet, you may be able to enlist the help of a specialist.

Board certified veterinary behaviorists are vets who undergo years of structured training in animal behavior after veterinary school and must pass a rigorous examination before being certified. They are trained to treat behavior problems as well as underlying medical problems and often work in tandem with a general vet and a credentialed dog trainer.

You can ask your vet to consult a veterinary behaviorist (many will consult with a general vet for no charge) or approach one yourself. The American College of Veterinary Behaviorists maintains online listings for these professionals in the United States (see dogdementia.com/linklist).

The vet behaviorist doesn't have to be local to you; many do consultations using Skype or video submissions, but only with the involvement of your general vet.

If your vet does not wish to participate, the veterinary behaviorist may be able to suggest a different vet close to you with whom he or she can partner to help your dog.

Seeing What We Want to See

Most studies are vulnerable to several types of bias. Studies that rely on observation, especially by untrained people, are especially so. Some of the studies cited above relied on the dogs' owners to gather information about behavioral changes. Having invested their time in a study, many owners are prone to want it to succeed. There are ways to compensate for bias, and these methods are an integral part of doing research. But there is no perfect study. Some initial successful results may be found later to be false or exaggerated. But as more studies are performed, the information will get more detailed and accurate.

In our daily life with our dogs, we are also vulnerable to bias. When we consult a vet and choose a treatment, we want it to work. We love our dogs. We have probably paid money for the chosen treatment. We are taking time to administer it to our dogs correctly. There are biases that can cause us to perceive improvement where there may be none (Kahneman 2011, 175-184). For example, a 2012 study showed that about 40 percent of the dog owners and nearly 45 percent of the participating veterinarians believed that an arthritic dog who was taking a placebo was improving (Conzemius and Evans 2012). This kind of belief can prevent us from looking for something more effective, and in some cases leave our dogs in unnecessary discomfort.

Keeping day-to-day notes about your dog's behavior will help you assess whether a treatment helps or not. Look especially for things you can count or measure. How many times did your dog eliminate in the house? How much time did she spend standing in corners? The more you can quantify, the better you can determine whether a treatment is working. There is more information on keeping records in chapter 7.

In the meantime, chapters 4 and 5 cover ways to keep your senior dog safe and enrich her life. Then we'll figure out some ways to keep *your* life as a caregiver as easy as possible.

References

Araujo, Joseph A., Marjorie L. Faubert, Melissa L. Brooks, Gary M. Landsberg, and Heidi Lobprise. 2012. "NOVIFIT®(NoviSAMe®) Tablets Improve Executive Function in Aged Dogs and Cats: Implications for Treatment of Cognitive Dysfunction Syndrome." *International Journal of Applied Research in Veterinary Medicine* 10 (1): 90.

Campbell, Sharon, Amy Trettien, and Brenda Kozan. 2001. "A Noncomparative Open-Label Study Evaluating the Effect of Selegiline Hydrochloride in a Clinical Setting." *Veterinary Therapeutics: Research In Applied Veterinary Medicine* 2 (1): 24-39.

Conzemius, Michael G., and Richard B. Evans. 2012. "Caregiver Placebo Effect for Dogs with Lameness from Osteoarthritis." *Journal of the American Veterinary Medical Association* 241 (10): 1314-1319.

Heath, Sarah Elizabeth, Stephen Barabas, and Paul Graham Craze. 2007. "Nutritional Supplementation in Cases of Canine Cognitive Dysfunction—A Clinical Trial." *Applied Animal Behaviour Science* 105 (4): 284-296.

Kahneman, Daniel. 2011. *Thinking, Fast and Slow.* New York: Farrar, Straus and Giroux.

Kealy, Richard D., Dennis F. Lawler, Joan M. Ballam, Sandra L. Mantz, Darryl N. Biery, Elizabeth H. Greeley, George Lust, Mariangela Segre, Gail K. Smith, and Howard D. Stowe. 2002. "Effects of Diet Restriction on Life Span and Age-Related Changes in Dogs." *Journal of the American Veterinary Medical Association* 220 (9): 1315-1320.

Landsberg, Gary. 2005. "Therapeutic Agents for the Treatment of Cognitive Dysfunction Syndrome in Senior Dogs." *Progress in Neuro-Psychopharmacology and Biological Psychiatry* 29 (3): 471-479.

Milgram, Norton W., Elizabeth Head, Steven C. Zicker, Candace Ikeda-Douglas, Heather Murphey, Bruce A. Muggenberg, Christina T. Siwak, P. Dwight Tapp, Stephen R. Lowry, and Carl W. Cotman. 2004. "Long-Term Treatment with Antioxidants and a Program of Behavioral Enrichment Reduces Age-Dependent Impairment in Discrimination and Reversal Learning in Beagle Dogs." *Experimental Gerontology* 39 (5): 753-765.

Milgram, Norton W., Gwen O. Ivy, Elizabeth Head, M. Paul Murphy, P. H. Wu, William W. Ruehl, Peter Yu, David Durden, Bruce Davis, Alick Paterson, and Alan Boulton. 1993. "The Effect of L-Deprenyl on Behavior, Cognitive Function, and Biogenic Amines in the Dog." *Neurochemical Research* 18 (12): 1211-1219.

Milgram, Norton W., Gary Landsberg, David Merrick, and Mark Y. Underwood. 2015. "A Novel Mechanism for Cognitive Enhancement in Aged Dogs with the Use of a Calcium-Buffering Protein." *Journal of Veterinary Behavior: Clinical Applications and Research* 10.3: 217-222.

Milgram, Norton W., Christina T. Siwak, Philippe Gruet, Patricia Atkinson, Frédérique Woehrlé, and Heather Callahan. 2000. "Oral Administration of Adrafinil Improves Discrimination Learning in Aged Beagle Dogs." *Pharmacology Biochemistry and Behavior* 66 (2): 301-305.

Milgram, Norton W., Steven C. Zicker, Elizabeth Head, Bruce A. Muggenburg, Heather Murphey, Candace J. Ikeda-Douglas, and Carl W. Cotman. 2002. "Dietary Enrichment Counteracts Age-Associated Cognitive Dysfunction in Canines." *Neurobiology of Aging* 23 (5): 737-745.

Nippak, Pria M. D., J. Mendelson, Bruce Muggenburg, and Norton W. Milgram. 2007. "Enhanced Spatial Ability in Aged Dogs Following Dietary and Behavioural Enrichment." *Neurobiology of Learning and Memory* 87 (4): 610-623.

Osella, Maria Cristina, Giovanni Re, Rosangela Odore, Carlo Girardi, Paola Badino, Raffaella Barbero, and Luciana Bergamasco. 2007. "Canine Cognitive Dysfunction Syndrome: Prevalence, Clinical Signs and Treatment with a Neuroprotective Nutraceutical." *Applied Animal Behaviour Science* 105 (4): 297-310.

Pan, Yuanlong, Brian Larson, Joseph A. Araujo, Winnie Lau, Christina De Rivera, Ruben Santana, Asa Gore, and Norton W. Milgram. 2010. "Dietary Supplementation with Medium-Chain TAG has Long-Lasting Cognition-Enhancing Effects in Aged Dogs." *British Journal of Nutrition* 103 (12): 1746-1754.

Rème, Christophe-Alexandre, Valerie Dramard, Laurent Kern, Joelle Hofmans, Christine Halsberghe, and D. Vida Mombiela. 2007. "Effect of S-Adenosylmethionine Tablets on the Reduction of Age-Related Mental Decline in Dogs: A Double-Blinded, Placebo-Controlled Trial." *Veterinary Therapeutics: Research in Applied Veterinary Medicine* 9 (2): 69-82.

Siwak, Christina T., Philippe Gruet, Frédérique Woehrlé, M. Schneider, Bruce A. Muggenburg, Heather L. Murphey, Heather Callahan, and Norton W. Milgram. 2000. "Behavioral Activating Effects of Adrafinil in Aged Canines." *Pharmacology Biochemistry and Behavior* 66 (2): 293-300.

Siwak, Christina T., Philippe Gruet, Frédérique Woehrlé, Bruce A. Muggenburg, Heather L. Murphey, and Norton W. Milgram. 2000. "Comparison of the Effects of Adrafinil, Propentofylline, and Nicergoline on Behavior in Aged Dogs." *American Journal of Veterinary Research* 61 (11): 1410-1414.

[4]

How to Help Your Dog: Setting Up Spaces, Routines, and Enrichment

This section covers the basics of setting up a safe space for your old dog, keeping track of her, and making her life interesting. This last is as important as the first two—unless your dog has very advanced canine cognitive dysfunction or another serious disease, she can probably still take some pleasure in life.

I mention helpful products in this chapter and the next couple. I've chosen not to include brand names because they change over time and so many new products are coming out. You can easily find the items I discuss by searching and using the names and terminology in these chapters.

A Safe Space

Foremost, you need to make your home and yard safe for your dog. This will be similar to puppy proofing.

Dogs with dementia can easily get stuck or trapped in furniture or fencing, or even get lost. They may start eliminating in inappropriate areas. And they may no longer be safe with other dogs. Your dog's needs will vary, depending on her symptoms and on her previous experience living with you.

She needs an environment that is safe and familiar. There should be places for food, water, and toileting and a comfortable bed. If she paces, she may need some room to walk around. At the same time, you need to eliminate hazards: sharp things she could bump into, things she could get tangled up in or stuck behind, and things she could fall off of. If you have other dogs, she may benefit from being able to see them, or need to be completely separated from them. Here are some possible setups.

For dogs who have been crate trained, love their crate, and are retaining their toilet abilities, the solution may be to start crating them more often. If your dog has had the run of the house for her adult life but is starting to get lost or stuck now, you can confine her when you leave the house just as you may have done when she was a puppy. Make sure the crate is safe, though. Don't leave a collar with tags on her if the tags could possibly get caught anywhere. Don't use a large-gauge wire crate that a small dog's legs could stick through. Don't use bedding that could catch her toenails. But also don't leave a slick plastic surface for a dog who is unsteady on her feet. Yes, it's tricky. And this is not an ideal solution for a dog who is driven to wander.

If your dog has lost her toileting skills, it gets more complicated. If she is steady on her feet and mostly gets confused about urinating, consider outfitting a bathroom with a combination of pee pads and washable bedding. You can try arranging it with the pee pads in one corner and the bedding in another, but this isn't a complete fix for a dog who is losing her housetraining. Whatever you set up will need frequent cleaning; you have merely localized the problem by putting your dog in a smaller space. Also be aware that small dogs can easily get trapped behind bathroom fixtures.

Stuck by the toilet

You may need to gate off the human toilet or block the back of it. And be sure there is no possibility your dog would jump into the bathtub. Your kitchen may be safer.

Arrangements can also get complicated for dogs who have multiple impairments. I will share my experience with Cricket, who was visually impaired, unsteady on her feet, and had lost her housetraining for defecation. Since she also paced, this combination meant that when I wasn't home she would pace, defecate, then walk back and forth in it until I returned. My work situation was such that I could get home in about 10 minutes. First, I installed a webcam so I could watch her when I was away from

A table support where Cricket got stuck

the house. (I discuss webcams below.) For the safe space, I fenced off part of a room for her with an unfolded exercise pen. The purpose of the fence was to prevent Cricket from getting caught among the legs of some furniture I had in the room. Before then, she'd had access to my study, where she had a bed that she still knew how to find. But the day I came home to find her crying, straddling one of the table supports (see page 47), I knew I could not make that extended space safe enough for her.

Since the hardwood floors in the fenced area were slick, I put down a mosaic of carpet runners and rubber backed rugs that wouldn't slide but also could be washed easily. I kept an eye on Cricket remotely and came home as soon as possible after she pooped to clean her feet, the floors, and the rugs.

Washable mats and rugs in the safe area with dangers fenced off

Please do not use an indoor electronic fence. They're associated with many problems for normal dogs, and on top of those, a dog with dementia will not be able to learn the cause-effect relationship between entering a certain area and getting a shock. Your dog will end up being shocked for behaviors she cannot avoid throughout the day and probably will still not stay in the safe area.

A partial list of things to remove, fence off, or change in a safe space:

- Steps
- Things with sharp corners
- Tangles of cables and wires
- Ramps

Ramps: unsafe for a wobbly or confused dog

- Support frameworks under tables or chairs

Furniture hazards

- Things that the dog used to be able to jump up on and may attempt to jump on again
- Wire crates or exercise pens in which the dog's legs could get caught
- Other dogs

About that last item: You know your dogs best. But in general, dogs with dementia can lose their ability to communicate with other dogs and to respond appropriately to situations and body language. Your dog's best doggie friend may get tired of being bumped into or approached when he doesn't want it. Play it safe.

I never allowed any dog to stay in Cricket's space when I wasn't there. When I was home, I let small, easygoing Zani mingle with her, but even that brought mishaps. Sometimes Zani would be in a dog bed and Cricket wouldn't see or realize it. Cricket would start trying to get in, literally walking on Zani, and Zani would bark and scare Cricket.

Products that can help you adapt a space for your dog and protect her from hazards include:

- Edge and corner guards. These are usually used in baby proofing to cover sharp areas on your furniture or built-in features of your home. They can be found in a variety of sizes.
- Cable conduit and cord covers. These can be found in electronics or office-supply stores and can eliminate tangles of cables.
- Gates. There are many kinds of baby gates available, as well as newer products designed for dogs. Even if your old dog is not very agile, if you have other dogs, the gate needs to be tall and sturdy enough to prevent them from coming into her space. Pay close attention to the space between bars on gates that have them. I had to measure and test many times before I was positive that Cricket could not put her head between the vertical bars of the gates I wanted.
- Crates and exercise pens. I've listed these items both under hazards and protective devices. The difference is the gauge of the wire. Small dogs can put a leg through the wires on large-gauge crates and pens. But products with less space between the wires can safely prevent your dog from encountering other hazards in the environment.

Tracking Tools

There are a number of tools available to help us keep track of our dogs' movements and thereby help keep them safe.

Webcams

Webcams are video cameras that transmit what is in their range over the Internet so it can be viewed from a remote location. They can be free-standing, built into computers or tablets, or created by repurposing a smartphone. Most require a Wi-Fi network where the webcam will be set up. You can then use another remote computer (say, at your workplace) or a smartphone or tablet to look in on your dog. Some webcams or applications that use webcams can be set to record or alert you if there is motion.

Elevated webcam

My webcam was a real help for me, as I've mentioned above. I got in the habit of looking in on Cricket every hour, or as often as possible, when I could. Not only could I see if she'd pooped, but I also knew quickly if she had gotten stuck or fallen over or had some other emergency. My webcam has repeatedly saved me time and stress in caring for all my dogs.

Motion Detectors

Some people use motion detectors to let them know if their dog has entered a certain part of the house. This works if other animals don't trigger it.

Locator Collars or Tags

Several brands of collars and tags contain transmitters that use GPS or radio signals to keep track of a pet's location. Some can send a warning if the animal leaves a certain defined area—for instance, if she jumps a fence. I hope most dogs with dementia are kept indoors for their own safety, but I mention these products for the rare situation where they might be appropriate or helpful.

Direct Observation (and Timers)

The very best protection is your own loving attention. Keep an eye on your oldster. If you tend to be forgetful (raises hand) you can set a timer or alarm when you're at home to remind you to check on your senior dog.

Routines

What do I mean by routines? If the dog eats at the same time every day, out of the same food toy or bowl, in the same place, that's a routine. If the human has a set schedule of work or other activities, and the dog stays in the same room when the human is gone and gets a treat when the human leaves for work, that's a routine. Human and dog may go on a walk at 4:30 every afternoon. They may have a play session in the backyard every morning when the weather is good. The dog may go out to potty every two hours, rain or shine.

Routines make life predictable. Predictability makes most dogs (and people) feel comfortable. Lack of predictability is linked to stress, which makes sense when you think about it.

But now repeat after me: "I can't force my dog to remember stuff."

My purpose is to caution you about false hope. You will read that it is important to keep up routines with your dog. Sure it is! As long as your dog remembers the routines, the predictability will be helpful. But when your dog forgets routines, they are no longer routines. You will need to assess for yourself how comfortable your dog is in the world when fewer and fewer things are predictable or understandable to her. And you will have to change your own routines to better care for your dog.

Things the dog has done thousands of times will likely be remembered longer than rarer behaviors (Bayles and Tomoeda 2013, 118). However, as your dog's cognitive decline progresses, even the most familiar behaviors and routines can be forgotten. Perhaps this is what gives rise to some of the anxiety that can come with dementia.

Imagine if you moved to another town, changed jobs, got divorced, and then remarried, all in a short time. You're living with someone new, whom you adore but whose habits you haven't yet learned, and let's throw in a couple teenage stepkids for good measure. You don't have a regular grocery store to go to. You have a new boss and coworkers. You can't even go to your favorite restaurant; it's in another town.

For most people, that would be very stressful. Now imagine if every day were like that, for the rest of your life. This is what dementia is like for a lot of people, and probably for dogs in their way. As they forget things, they become unmoored in life, and they can't learn new habits or routines to replace the old.

Some dogs probably weather this better than others. Cricket went through a few months of higher anxiety as her dementia increased, but later she relaxed. She bobbed around in life and didn't seem bothered by her condition.

Enrichment: Use That Brain or Lose It

Or use it and lose it more slowly.

Why am I being such a wet blanket? Because the problem here is that your dog is forgetting things and losing the ability to learn new things. All the enrichment in the world can't stanch that decline forever, as far as we know. At some point, neither veterinary medicine nor your most dedicated efforts will help. But you may be able to slow down the process.

In chapter 3, I discussed the research on enrichment. The elderly beagles in an experiment were taught a behavior using positive reinforcement, given toys to play with, and got some exercise. This was pretty basic enrichment, but resulted in better retention of cognitive skills as the dogs aged.

What enrichment can you give a dog who is already losing some cognitive function? Nothing too difficult, and nothing that will scare or frustrate her. For instance, this is not a good time in her life to begin agility lessons or try to teach her to swim. But if she already loves to swim, are there safe water games you can play at home? Does she like to play in the spray of a hose or sprinkler? Can she safely play with toys or bob for floating treats in a kiddie pool?

Does she like digging? Can you make her a sandbox and bury some fun stuff?

And then there are scent games. If you look at a diagram of a dog brain (see dogdementia.com/linklist), you will see a sizable portion called the olfactory bulb. It's three times the size of the human counterpart, even though our brains are much bigger. Dogs are practically noses on legs. Games and activities based on scent and finding/eating food tend to be very satisfying to them.

For some readers, it may be a new idea to encourage your dog to work for some of her food. It may even seem a little mean or unfair. But most dogs love these activities. Think of the fun children can have searching for Easter eggs, or the joy that working puzzles gives some adults. Most dogs also enjoy solving problems for an immediate reward, such as food. Most important is to start with an easy puzzle where the dog can have quick success.

Homemade Food Games

The easiest food game is to lay out your dog's dry food or treats around the room for her to find. Make a trail for the dog to follow, scatter the kibble around the room, or, as your dog gains some skill at the game, try hiding some. I scattered food for Cricket until near the end of her life. I used food that was easy to see and smell and I put it in areas of high visual contrast (dark treats on a white rug, for example). Cricket found it as she wandered around.

Another, only slightly more challenging "game" to make with materials from around the house: Put some dry food or healthy, easy-to-clean-up treats in a cardboard box that's the right size for your dog to be able to root around in and top it off with some wadded-up nontoxic paper, like butcher paper. Let your dog work to get the food out. You can make it easier (put in just a bit of paper she has to push out of the way) or harder (hide some of the food in the wadded-up paper), depending on her capabilities. Supervise so she doesn't consume the paper or cardboard.

If you have a retriever-type dog, or any dog who is apt to pick up a ball, you can make a game using a muffin tin. Use a clean tin and as many balls as there are sockets in the tin. Put some attractive food in each of the sockets, then put a tennis ball on top of each. When the dog lifts up the ball and drops it elsewhere, the food becomes available. People often set this up as a guessing game, putting food in only one or a few of the sockets. For a dog with cognitive dysfunction though, it's best to fill every socket. You want to make it extra easy to win the game.

Puppy Toys

Many food toys are probably too hard for your dog now, but what about the ones for puppies? Some will yield food at the slightest touch (see dogdementia.com/linklist). Give it a go, and if your dog still seems frustrated, stop. Choose something that is safe for your dog—nothing she can chew up and ingest, for

Cricket getting food out of a toy

example. Here's Cricket rolling a Kong puppy toy around.

And you can check out the video I made that shows how to start puppies and inexperienced dogs out with easy food toys: "Kongs for Beginners" (see dogdementia.com/linklist). But if your dog has no experience with food toys or always has food available, this may still be too difficult.

Scent Activities

If you did any trained scenting activities with your dog when she was younger, such as tracking or nose work, you can continue to do easier versions throughout your dog's senior years. But even for dogs who aren't familiar with structured scent activities, there are ways to use scent as enrichment.

First, even if your dog isn't very ambulatory, you can take her somewhere where there are new smells. (This assumes she is OK in the car and not anxious in new places.) I took Cricket on a little walk through the neighborhood every day until she no longer had the cognitive ability to walk with me. But after that, she still enjoyed smells. So I would just accompany her into the front yard and let her wander around.

The very easiest way to bring a bit of enrichment into the life of a dog who is curious about scents is simply to let her smell everything new you bring into the house. It doesn't need to be food. It can be a new sweater from the department store, some sandpaper from the hardware store, or anything at all that isn't

toxic or dangerous. And of course bags of groceries are prime. Let your dog sniff, safely, as long as she wants.

Getting a good sniff

"Big Adventure Time"

Renowned agility competitor Susan Garrett coined the phrase "big adventure time" for the enrichment activities she does with her retired dogs, who always remain beloved family pets. She makes sure her oldsters get to do something special every day: a ride in the car, a walk to the mailbox, a slow-motion tug session, or a swim.

Associate certified applied animal behaviorist Kathy Sdao recommends something similar, including taking your senior dog's meal "on the road" and having a picnic somewhere safe and pleasant.

These ideas are aimed at dogs who still have most of their cognitive abilities, but they can be scaled down for dogs with dementia as well. I am convinced that part of the reason Cricket thrived as long as she did was that she continued to go to work with me several days a week. It was a safe but different environment, and even the car ride broke up her day and gave her some sensory stimulation.

Routines Versus Enrichment

You may have noticed these two types of activities oppose each other. Routines make your dog's life predictable. Enrichment introduces variety.

You are the expert on your own dog, and can balance these goals accordingly. For Cricket, I tried to bring in as much enrichment as possible while keeping her feeling safe. We don't want our dogs to feel anxious or be overwhelmed.

Changing Your Own Behavior

Even if your dog is a very easy keeper, you will need to change your own behavior as her family member and caregiver. Making a lot of behavioral changes can be stressful. I made lists of the things I had to do differently to take good care of Cricket. The act of thinking things through and writing them down helped solidify the new behaviors and reduce my stress.

Here is the initial list I came up with. Depending on your dog's particular needs and how advanced her dementia is, your list may be longer.

- Open doors carefully.
- Let your dog see you.
- Keep her in sight.
- Run interference with or separate her from other dogs.
- Read new signals she may give before she eliminates.
- Take her out to eliminate on a schedule.
- Go with her every time she is in the yard.
- Monitor her food and fluid intake and help her eat and drink if needed.
- Determine other needs she may have and not be able to communicate with you.
- Carry her when she has difficulty walking, or support her if she is a large breed.
- Develop more skill in handling, such as for administering medication or grooming.
- Change your schedule, or your family's schedule, so someone is home more frequently than before.
- Devise systems for cleanup that keep things easy for you.

Giving your dog's environment this extra thought will help keep her safe. Enrichment may strengthen her mind and even help her live longer. But she may still have more specific issues in her daily life that require planning and preparation on your part. That's what I'll cover in the next chapter.

[5]

How to Help Your Dog: Specific Challenges

Canine cognitive dysfunction can cause difficulties in many aspects of your dog's life. Eating, drinking, sleeping, eliminating—behaviors that you used to be able to take for granted—can become challenging for your dog. And in turn, that can make taking care of your dog a lot harder. This section includes ideas, methods, and products that can help maintain (or even improve) your dog's quality of life and maybe your own too.

Drinking

If your dog has difficulty drinking, first check with your vet to rule out any problems unrelated to dementia. Then you will need to observe your dog to figure out how to help her drink.

Elevating the water source can sometimes do the trick, but don't use a waterer with a wire base that she could get a foot stuck in or tip over. When Cricket started having a hard time drinking, I elevated her bowl. Then when she began to walk into it and knock it over, I got a waterer with a plastic tank and shallow bowl and put that on a three-inch book. She still managed

Elevated waterer placed in a corner

to tip it over once or twice, but not so often as with the bowl. A large, shallow bowl can be good for dogs who have trouble aiming their snouts at the water, and the shallowness lessens the possibility of a frail dog drowning.

Cricket finally forgot how to drink water. Raising her bowl helped and gave her a few more months of drinking on her own, but as her cognition continued to decline she would walk to the waterer and just stand there and stare. She did not drink water on her own for the last six weeks of her life. I gave her small bowls of milk and unsalted homemade chicken broth and held them for her if she needed me to. And every day I mixed water or one of those liquids into her wet food to make a kind of soup. I am proud to say that she stayed completely hydrated. It just took some attention on my part.

Caution: Elevated bowls can be contraindicated in breeds prone to bloat, including (but not limited to) Akitas, basset hounds, bloodhounds, boxers, collies, German shepherds, Great Danes, Great Pyrenees, Irish setters, Irish wolfhounds, Labrador retrievers, Old English sheepdogs, shar-peis, Saint Bernards, standard poodles, and Weimaraners. If you have one of these breeds, or a mixed-breed dog with a deep-chested physique, check with your vet about whether it is safe to elevate the water or food bowl.

Eating

I was lucky that Cricket remained a good eater until the day she died. But I do have some experience with appetite loss in pets.

If your dog is having trouble eating, or his appetite seems to be declining, the first thing to do is see a veterinarian to rule out a separate medical problem. Physical issues ranging from dental to gastrointestinal can affect eating behavior. Don't assume your dog is just being picky; she might be in pain.

But a second possibility is that your dog has already trained you to offer progressively more attractive foods. He may have learned that if he refuses what you put down, you will provide something he likes better. This behavior may continue even as he grows older and loses cognitive function. I hope you can find something for your dog that is both healthy and enjoyable. If he remains particular, you will have more of a challenge making sure he hasn't lost his appetite.

Finally, as with drinking, canine cognitive dysfunction can cause dogs to lose many of the skills involved in eating. If this happens to your dog, there are a couple things you can try.

Filled food tubes

First, provide something easier to eat. If he eats kibble, you can switch to canned food. If he eats raw food, including bones, you may need to change to a ground raw diet. Some dogs will suck food out of food tubes such as those pictured.

You can make a paste out of most foods by processing them with some liquid. See more ideas under "Taking Medicine" below.

Even though you should keep nutrition in mind, you may not be able to get your dog to eat an ideal diet for his last few weeks or months. It may boil down to whatever he is willing and able to eat. If it does, the nutritional quality of his diet may be one factor in your decision-making process about his quality of life.

Second, you can try making a change in the feeding setup. If your dog paces or stumbles around, a good option is to put his food and water in a corner (or possibly in separate corners).

Elevated bowls in a corner

Spills will be less likely. But even more important, the corner acts as a barrier to keep your dog from walking on through the food. Cricket tended to walk forward when she leaned forward to eat and would just walk on over a bowl and keep going if there was nothing to stop her. Then she couldn't find the bowl she had just been eating out of. She did best with a slightly elevated food bowl, as with the water. (Remember, elevated bowls may be contraindicated for some breeds—check the list on page 62.)

Although I don't normally leave food out for my dogs, I did so for Cricket when her dementia became advanced. I often left some goodies in her elevated bowl in a corner. And as mentioned previously, I also scattered a handful of high-quality, strong-smelling food (fish kibble or semimoist food roll) on a white rug before I left. She saw and smelled well enough to find most of it, and it gave her something to do. She was able to eat that way till the end of her life.

Elimination

Your dog may become like a puppy again in the most inconvenient way—and now he will make bigger messes.

Problems with elimination are common with dementia. A noticeable loss of housetraining is a typical sign, and quantifying elimination incidents is one way the level of dementia is measured in surveys and studies. One of the drug studies for canine cognitive dysfunction listed the specific scenario of a previously housetrained dog coming in from outside and eliminating right in front of the owner (Campbell, Trettien, and Kozan 2001). That's a big tip-off.

That said, it is important to distinguish this from possible physical problems, which could include age-related incontinence or an underlying medical condition. Also, gastrointestinal problems can manifest as changes in the stool and/or frequency of bowel movements. Care must be taken that what we perceive as a cognitive problem is not masking a medical condition. Check with your vet on this. (Are you detecting a theme yet?)

With dementia, housetraining tends to decline in stages. If your dog has a way to ask to go outside, that may be the first thing he forgets. You will need to take him out regularly, as you would a puppy, staying aware of his habits and observing any signals he does give. Dogs with dementia will also soil their crates, even if they have never done so before.

If forgetting how to ask to go outside were the only problem, it wouldn't be too bad. But your dog may also forget that he should eliminate when he is outside. As in the drug-study

Wiling to "go" in the snow

scenario, he may spend five or 10 minutes toddling around outdoors, then eliminate immediately upon entering the house.

Please be patient with your dog. He can't help it. He's not try-ing to spite or defy you. Especially, please don't punish him for it.

Dogs can lose their housetraining for urination, defecation, or both. I have read that urination is more common, but my little Cricket was the opposite. Until the day she died, she would im-mediately pee when I took her outside. Since I took her out a lot, she rarely had urine accidents in the house.

But she pooped in the house every other day or so, and as noted above, she would then pace through the poop again and again. If I wasn't there to intervene, I would come home to find a mix of feces and carpet fuzz lodged between her paw pads.

I dealt with this two ways. The first step for both was to put on disposable gloves. If there was just a bit of poop on one foot, I used baby wipes to clean it. But if there was a lot of poop, I ran lukewarm water in a sturdy plastic dishpan dedicated to that task and stood Cricket in it. With the gloves on, I dislodged the poop from each paw in turn, changing the water as many times as needed.

In preparation for ordeals like these, it is a good idea to ac-custom your dog to lots of body-handling and grooming scenar-ios before she declines cognitively. See "Desensitization and Counterconditioning to Handling" below.

There are some products that can help with elimination difficulties.

Diapers

Diapers are available for male and female dogs of all sizes, as disposables or washables with a disposable pad. Do-it-yourselfers can make dog diapers out of boys' briefs by insert-ing all or part of a human incontinence pad.

If overused, or used without attention to hygiene, they can cause further problems for your dog. But occasional, careful use of a well-fitted diaper can be helpful.

If you use diapers on your dog, in most cases you will need to shave or trim the hair around the dog's genital and anal area. Having either urine or feces caught in the hair can cause problems including irritation and infections.

Some commercially produced diapers are sized by weight and waist size of your dog, and with others you will need to do some guesswork. There is at least one variety (Tinkle Trousers) available for giant breeds.

The website Vetinfo has a good guide to using diapers for your dog that focuses on hygiene and health concerns.

Blogger Roxanne Hawn shares advice about making your own dog diapers at her blog, *Champion of My Heart.* See dogdementia.com/linklist for links to both of these articles.

Belly Bands

Belly bands are for male dogs only. They are used to absorb urine. The cautions about diapers also apply here. Most belly

bands are washable and designed to be used without an extra pad. Fitted correctly, they are less intrusive and probably more comfortable than most diapers.

Belly band

Pee Pads

These absorbent pads, to be placed on the floor indoors, are frequently used for puppies or small dogs. There are both washable and disposable types. You can even try the washable bed pads designed for humans. Pee pads never worked for Cricket, but if your dog knows how to use them already, they may continue to be useful during cognitive decline. Just be aware that if your dog wanders, she may accidentally catch the edges and drag the pads around.

Hygiene

Senior dogs' immune systems get weaker along with their bones, joints, and organs. Be vigilant about veterinary care for wounds or illnesses. Dogs who have switched to mostly soft food may also be more prone to tooth decay and mouth infections. Incontinence issues add to the health risks. Use common sense about keeping your dog and her environment clean.

I mentioned earlier that I sometimes left food out for Cricket. This could be leftover canned food in her bowl (which also turned out to be delectable to ants) or pieces of drier food strewn around for her to find. If you do the latter, remember that your dog may have lost any former inhibitions about eating and eliminating in the same area. And if your dog is very small, it may be hard to distinguish poop from little pieces of dog food. If I left food on the floor for Cricket, when I returned I threw away anything that was left, no questions asked.

Sleeping

Sleep problems can present some of the most difficult challenges for caretakers of a dog with dementia.

My three best tips:

- Do everything you can to provide some exercise and mental stimulation during the day. Walk her if she can walk. Allow her to pace if it is safe. Hide some favorite food (safely) for her to walk around and find. If she can still play training games, train. If she enjoys riding in the car, take her with you, even if just to a drive-through. (Don't leave her in the car by herself.) I was fortunate to be able to take Cricket to work with me, which provided a change of scenery and kept her in practice riding in the car. (I used a very small crate in the car with a cushy bed so she wouldn't try to sit up, as she wasn't strong enough to hold herself steady when the car turned.) My office was not open to the public, so for her it was a stress-free home away from home.

"Office dog" in her younger days

- Have a contingency plan for times when she is too restless to settle down. Cricket usually slept with me in my bed, but her particular problem at night was that she would startle while asleep and sit bolt upright. After that, she sometimes got up and moved around, and was at risk of walking off the bed. And sometimes that was an indicator that she had to eliminate. So you can bet it woke me instantly. Several times in the last months of her life, I put her on the floor and let her walk the hall. I hated to do it, because she preferred to be with me. But I needed to get some sleep.
- Once again, talk to your vet. There are pharmaceutical interventions that can help many dogs. It is a kindness to explore this. Your dog's sleep problems may stem from anxiety, and treating them with a prescription drug may help her during the day as well.

Dog Beds

Unless you have a large or heavy-coated breed, your dog will probably prefer a bed to the bare floor. My dogs have different bed preferences. Cricket liked anything soft. She also liked to be under the covers, but couldn't get under them on her own even when she had all her marbles. My dog Zani rolls herself up in a blanket. Summer lies on one of my bed pillows. Clara likes anything cushy.

You probably know what kind of beds your dog likes (and she may like different kinds at different times). But if your dog has dementia, you will have to figure out whether her favorite beds remain safe and where to put them. If the "safe space" you have set up includes a place where your dog already has a bed, that's great. If you create a new space, try to put the bed somewhere easy to find. Dogs with dementia tend to end up by walls or in corners a lot. Cricket did. But towards the end of her life, when she was extremely unsteady on her feet, I discovered that if I put a donut-type bed in the middle of her space, she would often trip over it, land in there, and go to sleep. It was soft and safe (no fringe or anything she could get her feet or nails caught in), so I went with it.

Two easy-to-find beds in the safe room

People Beds

The main considerations about dogs sleeping in their owners' beds are safety and hygiene. If your dog has always slept with you, you may be able to work something out. You will need to ensure that your dog won't fall off, get in trouble with other animals, or make messes that are difficult to clean. But don't assume that staying in the bed will be the best option. At some point, you may need to make another arrangement for your dog's safety.

Cricket had always liked to sleep under the covers. As her dementia progressed, she wasn't happy covered up anymore, but still wanted to be very close to me. I made a barrier of pillows she could lean up against and kept towels on top of and under the bedding in the places she was most likely to sleep, since she sometimes leaked a little urine.

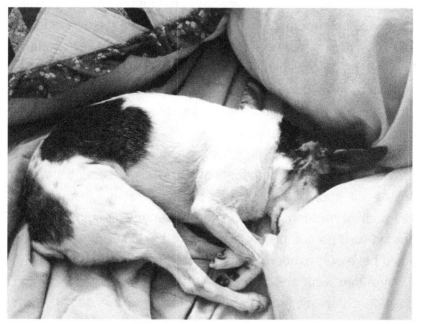

Cricket and the pillow barrier

It was important in our situation to keep the other dogs away, both because of Cricket's frailty and because her odd behavior could possibly provoke them. Two of my other three dogs were crated at night. Summer had never gotten along with Cricket and had the potential to be aggressive, and Clara was a big, pushy puppy almost four times Cricket's size. Zani was allowed free, because she was small and good natured and knew to stay away from Cricket (no doubt because of all the dirty looks Cricket shot her early in their lives together).

The arrangement with Cricket loose on the bed worked because I was a light sleeper and woke up whenever she did, because she was not a night wanderer, and because I could control other factors to keep her safe.

Getting Around

There are many products available to help animals with mobility problems. Unfortunately, anything that requires the dog to learn new cognitive or motor skills must be ruled out for dementia. That means devices like ramps, step stools, and wheels probably won't work. Dogs with CCD are already forgetting things they have known all of their lives, and their retention of new information can be almost nil.

Some dogs with rear-end weakness like Cricket had can get fitted with wheels, but probably not if they have dementia. When Cricket got stuck in a corner, the problem was not just that she was poor at backing up. It was that she couldn't figure out she needed to. The complexity involved in backing up with wheels would have only exacerbated the problem.

What can work are devices that help you help your dog and those that improve traction without requiring the dog to learn new behavior.

Mobility Slings

These consist of wide straps that run under your dog's belly with handles on each end. You can use them to help your dog up inclines, or keep him from tripping or falling as he walks on different surfaces.

Strollers

Strollers made for dogs with mobility problems are surprisingly reasonably priced. Dogs who enjoy walks can be transitioned into a stroller if they develop difficulties walking due to mobility or confusion. And they're not just for small dogs—some are rated to carry up to 150 pounds.

Lift Harnesses

These specially designed harnesses have a built-in handle on the back and are designed to support your dog safely when you lift him.

Traction or Nonslip Footwear

These shoes or boots fit over the dog's feet and are usually secured around the ankles. There are also socks with treads that are designed for indoor wear. They are helpful for some dogs with dementia, but for others the change in how the dog needs to walk is too great. If they are used, the dog needs to be supervised to be sure she doesn't remove or chew them.

Traction Toenail Covers

These are clever covers for the dog's toenails. They can be a great help, again, if the dog can adjust to them and doesn't pull them off. For some dogs they emulate natural traction very well.

Flooring with Traction

If you don't have floors the dog can walk on without slipping, you can create them. This was the single most important thing for Cricket. With her confusion and rear-end weakness, she could not navigate even a moderately smooth floor. I used washable bath mats and a carpet runner for the long hall she tended to wander up and down. These were good alternatives to permanent carpet, because she was partly incontinent.

Runners and rugs for pacing

Yoga mats also provide great traction and are easy on the paws. Most can be machine washed if you take them out before the spin cycle. There are now textured treads that can be applied with adhesive to smooth flooring, similar to traction treads on stairs. Outdoors in colder climates, textured "ice carpets" can be laid over snow and ice.

Space to Pace

When your dog first starts to pace or wander, it can be disturbing. But in Cricket's case, after I got used to it and could really watch her body language, it was my conclusion that she was not distressed. (Your dog's mileage may vary, so watch for potential signs of anxiety.) I was glad I could arrange a space where she could naturally wander up and down a hall. It was good exercise for her, and I think it contributed to her moderately calm nights.

Remember to control access to stairways, ramps the dog can fall off of, and doggie doors. All of these can pose problems for a dog with cognitive deficits and/or mobility problems.

Desensitization and Counterconditioning to Handling

As our dogs grow older, we generally need to handle them more. By "handling" I mean not just petting but brushing, trimming, and shaving; cutting nails; examining teeth, ears, and eyes; and other kinds of interactions many dogs dislike. The need for handling is even greater with dogs who have dementia: they just need more physical help from us.

For teaching your dog to accept and even enjoy handling, there is a straightforward, pleasant method. It is called desensitization and counterconditioning, or DS/CC. If your dog is in the early stages of dementia, it's not too late to start. And even if her cognitive function has deteriorated such that she has lost the ability to make lasting associations, these methods can at least distract her in the moment.

Getting a Baseline

Observing how comfortable your dog is with handling is important. If your dog has dementia she may startle more easily or be more generally sensitive, in addition to having the typical aches and pains of an older dog. The first step in helping her accept and enjoy handling is to learn about her current responses.

Owners often completely miss signs of stress in their dogs. Here is how to get a sense of how comfortable your dog is with various kinds of handling. I'm going to use the example of picking up a small dog, but it can be applied to any handling situation. The corollary with a larger dog could be lifting his front end, then back end, to help him into the car.

Perform the following exercise only if you already pick up your dog frequently and it is safe for both of you.

Use a video camera or a smartphone to record the session. Ask someone to help you, or use a tripod. Without too much fuss, position the camera in front of your dog to film the face and front of the body. Turn it on, then walk up, letting your dog see you, and pick her up. Hold her for up to 10 seconds, then put her down. Repeat with the camera in the same position but this time walk up from behind the dog if this is safe.

You can use a similar process to test different kinds of handling you regularly do with your dog.

Now study the videos. Your job is to look for behaviors that indicate discomfort, including licking the lips, yawning, panting, turning the head away, ducking the head, showing the whites of the eyes, stiffening, pulling away, and struggling. (The 4Paws University website has an excellent page called "Stress Signs in Dogs" that shows most of these. See dogdementia.com/linklist.) View your video in slow motion if you can. Many of these behaviors are very quick.

If your dog is exhibiting any of these behaviors, pay attention to when they are happening. In the picking up example, she may struggle when your hands tighten around her but snuggle in once you have her. Or she may appear relaxed when being picked up, but struggle if you hold her for more than a second.

The following photos are video stills of this exercise with Cricket. Take a look at the photos and see what you think about how comfortable she was.

Picking up Cricket #1

Picking up Cricket #2

The video from which these were taken is also available for viewing: "Counterconditioning: What You Condition is What You Get" (see dogdementia.com/linklist).

Cricket's body language showed stress from the moment I leaned over to pick her up. She continued to show it while I lifted her and while I held her.

So I used desensitization and counterconditioning to help change her response. You can do the same with your dog with things that bother her.

How It Works

Can you remember a sound from your childhood that came to predict something you liked? I can think of two right away: the sound of popcorn kernels being poured into a measuring cup and the sound of my dad's keys when he came home from work. Neither sound was meaningful the day I was born, but as I grew up, since they were always followed by something I liked—eating popcorn or getting to see my dad—the sounds themselves began to elicit the same happy responses. (The process works the same way for unpleasant associations, which is also important to know when teaching dogs about handling.)

Dogs make associations just like we do. What signals does your dog notice that predict supper? The clang of a bowl, the opening of a sack or can? Does his tail start to wag? Does he perhaps even drool?

The name for what we are talking about here is classical conditioning, sometimes called Pavlovian conditioning. Pavlov discovered that if a previously meaningless signal preceded meat enough times, dogs started to salivate at the signal, just as they would when presented with food.

We can use this to influence a dog's response to signals that already have taken on a negative association as well. Repeatedly pairing something the animal likes, generally food, with something the animal dislikes, often called the trigger, can change the animal's response to it. This is called counterconditioning.

In a classical conditioning or counterconditioning procedure, the dog is not required to do a particular behavior to earn the food. The focus is on teaching the dog that the scary stimulus predicts the food.

Desensitization, the other process at work, is gradual exposure, starting with the trigger at a level of intensity that does not elicit the unwanted response. As the dog gets comfortable, we work up to the full intensity in small steps, just as we might acclimate a child to a swimming pool by first encouraging him to put his toe in the water.

People use DS/CC to teach dogs to accept and enjoy all sorts of handling, including:

- Ear, eye, and mouth exams
- Application of topical medications
- Paw handling
- Nail trimming or grinding
- Tooth brushing
- Rectal exams or insertion of a thermometer
- Injections
- Putting on walking equipment or clothing
- Lifting into and onto things

With older dogs, we often need to do more grooming, more husbandry, more picking up, and more acclimation to equipment.

How to Do It

Let's say you want your dog to respond happily to having her foot touched. The sequence for counterconditioning goes like this:

- Touch - treat - wait at least 20 seconds
- Touch - treat - wait at least 20 seconds
- Touch - treat - wait at least 20 seconds

Don't always make the wait period the same length. Varying the time in between repetitions will make the relationship of the action to the treat more clear (Lavond and Steinmetz 2003, 8).

Most important, the touch should predict the food. Get it backwards and you can turn the presentation of the food into a warning. So touch, *then* treat, then wait a while. Deliver the food in a timely way, but don't startle the dog with it; a gap of up to about a second between the touch and the treat is OK.

Keep the food somewhere very accessible to you where the dog can't get it. In a bowl on a counter works, or in a loose pocket or treat pouch. Make sure you can get a piece out smoothly and efficiently with minimal fuss. If you need to have it your hand already to get the timing right, keep that hand out of sight or still until after you touch.

It's also important to start with a version of the handling that the dog is OK with. (This is the desensitization part.) If your dog panics when his feet are handled, you could grab a foot and give a treat a hundred times, but the dog might not change his mind about foot handling. You have to start off in a situation where the dog can keep his wits about him. (This state is sometimes called "under threshold.") If he hates having his foot grabbed, start by reaching towards him but stopping before getting to his foot, then giving him a treat. If even that's too much, start by sitting down next to him (then treat) or looking at his foot (then treat).

After the dog looks happy about, or at least like he is anticipating a treat as a result of, that action, you can progress to
something a little closer to your goal. You can go from looking
at the foot to reaching towards it to touching it lightly to touching
it a little more firmly to a longer touch to a tiny bit of paw ma-
nipulation, etc.

Each step may take many repetitions, over a number of
days, especially if your dog has a history of finding touching unpleasant. Or the process may go very quickly. Whatever the
rate of progress, if you are careful never to rush ahead of the
dog, these sessions can be a very pleasant experience for him.

I suggest you pick one type of handling at a time to work on.
Refer back to your videos to choose what might be most helpful. Whatever you choose, repeat each step until you see a
positive difference in your dog's response. Once you have done
that successfully you may want to branch out and make other
types of handling more enjoyable for your dog.

My video entitled "Using Desensitization/Counterconditioning
for Applying Flea Medicine" shows an example of the method
being applied (see dogdementia.com/linklist).

Practical Examples

If your dog has dementia and also some kind of sensory loss,
such as deafness or visual impairment, it helps to have a way to
get the dog's attention without startling her. With my dog
Cricket, I used a feather-light tap to her rear end—the equiva-
lent of tapping a person on the shoulder to get his or her attention. We all know that can be annoying, and an annoyed or
startled dog might be moved to bite. So I wanted to make this
kind of tap pleasant for Cricket.

Every day I prepared several really good treats: cheese or
meat. Then I went to Cricket and got in front of her, where she

could see me. I reached out and tapped her rear end, then gave her a treat. When I reached for her I would make sure I wasn't reaching over her head or otherwise coming close to her face. Reach and tap, treat. Wait. Reach and tap, treat. I would do three to eight of these repetitions per day.

After a couple weeks of that, I started touching her from behind when she didn't know I was there. She startled of course, but when she turned towards me I stuck the treat in her mouth. I was also still doing sets of the previous version where she could see me. After a week of that, she was starting to react by anticipating the treat, rather than jumping from nervousness. I did the same exercise when she was lying down.

Eventually her reaction to being touched was to turn eagerly towards me, looking for her treat. Note that I wasn't training her to turn around when I touched her. I was teaching her to anticipate something nice when she was touched, rather than to startle. Her eager turn to me was a side effect of the method.

I also counterconditioned my way of picking Cricket up. Sometimes we can't get a dog all the way to joyfulness with a certain type of handling, but we can get her happier than when she started. This was true for Cricket. Over about two months she moved from being startled to calm acceptance of being picked up. She did move all the way to enjoyment for being held.

I remember much earlier in her life telling a friend that carrying Cricket was like carrying a spider—she was all wriggling legs. That never would have changed if I hadn't actively worked to make being held a pleasant experience for her. In the last year of Cricket's life, the elevator in my office building had to be replaced. For most of a summer, I had to walk up three flights to my office at least twice a day. Going to work with me was such an important part of Cricket's life that I wasn't willing to give it up. So I carried her, carefully, hanging onto the railing with my other hand, up and down all those flights of stairs. And she was quiet and perfectly content tucked under my arm, perching on my hip.

Taking Medicine

The time to teach your dog to take a pill is before she is old and sick and finicky. If your dog is still eating well, you can start preparing *now*. You can buy empty capsules of different sizes at many health food stores for practice.

Of course, we humans have a tendency to wait until we have a problem, rather than being proactive early on. Fortunately, some of the methods below will also work without prior training.

Peanut butter and canned cat food are the old standbys for administering pills. Try putting the medicine in a spoonful of one or the other and offering the conglomeration to your dog. Coconut oil is a newcomer to the "pill disguise club," and many people report great success when coating pills with it as well. You can also buy commercially made pill pockets that many dogs really enjoy. But some dogs are wise to these methods. If a coating of something fantastic doesn't work, here are four other methods to try.

Meatball Method

Get some little meatballs. Seriously. You can buy a package of them premade and frozen. Just be sure they are cooked. (True story: I got amazing performance from Summer during several agility lessons using beef and pork meatballs as treats. Only when I threw the bag away did I realize they had been raw.)

OK. Do this a couple times without a pill first.

Thaw a frozen meatball and cut it in half. (For a larger dog, you can use whole meatballs.) Put a meatball half in each hand. Wave your hands and show your dog and get her excited:

"Lookie here! I have meatballs! Yum! Do you want them?" Make sure she knows that you have a piece in each hand.

When she is really excited about the meatball, give her one of the halves. Immediately, before she has even bitten down, stick the other half right in front of her. Most dogs will gulp the first piece in order to get the second. Repeat.

After your dog is happily gulping the first meatball half to get to the second, embed the pill in half a meatball. Give it to her first, then follow up with the plain piece.

Meatball half with pill embedded

If your dog is already pill savvy, use three to five meatball halves. Deliver them rapid-fire to your dog, chattering happily if that gets your dog eating faster. Start and end the process with plain ones and put the one with the pill in the middle.

For the pill-savvy dog, there is a risk that the routine, including any chatter, will come to predict pills in the meatballs. It's good insurance to keep doing meatball sessions without any pills as well.

My video on YouTube shows the basic process: "How To Give Your Dog a Pill Using the Multiple Meatball Method" (see dogdementia.com/linklist).

Squeeze-Tube Method

This method, which is best for small or medium-size pills, takes a little practice before you can use it in real life. I just happened onto it because I already used food in tubes for training treats.

Buy some food-grade squeeze tubes. One brand is Coghlan's (see photo on page 63). You can get them online at REI or Amazon, among other places. You may also find some decent ones at a discount store. Just make sure you get tubes that are specifically intended for food, so the plastic is safe.

Fill a tube with something squeezable that your dog really likes. You can use canned dog food, as long as it's not chunky. You can make mixtures of foods like cream cheese, canned pumpkin, peanut butter, and/or tuna that has been run through a food processor. (Perhaps not all of those together, though then again your dog would probably like that.) You may need to experiment a little to get the right texture. Too runny and it will be a mess. Too thick and you can't get it out.

The post entitled "The Secret to Filling a Food Tube" on my blog has sample recipes and instructions on how to get the right consistency (see dogdementia.com/linklist).

Teach your dog to eat out of the tube while you squeeze it. This is not usually difficult. After you put the great stuff in there, take the cap off the tube and let your dog smell it. He will probably start to lick it. Then you can gently squeeze the tube. Give him a couple squeezes a day for a week or two. (Refrigerate the tube in between sessions, and clean it out and replace the filling as necessary to ensure that the contents are fresh and safe.) He will learn that great stuff comes out of the tube, and that the best way to eat it is just to open his mouth and let you squeeze it in.

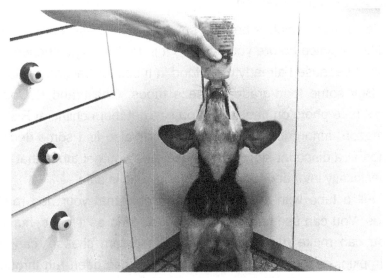

A food tube delivering very good stuff to Zani

After your dog has learned to eat from the tube, administering pills is usually a cinch. Prepare your tube and squeeze it so some of the mixture moves into the neck, about to come out. Stick the pill down in it. If you think you need to, smear a little food on top of the pill to disguise it. Offer the tube to the dog. As he opens his mouth and starts to lick, squeeze. The pill rides in, pushed by the food behind it.

My public video entitled "Some Easy Ways for Dogs to Take Pills" shows the food tube method of administering pills and a similar method using commercial spray cheese (see dogdementia.com/linklist).

Syringe Method

This is a variant of the squeeze-tube method. Some dogs will accept a syringe of liquid better than they do a dry pill, disguised or not.

Get some syringes (without needles!) from your vet or pharmacy. Check with your vet to make sure that it's OK to grind up your dog's pill and whether it's OK for you to touch the resulting powder. She may advise you to wear gloves. Get a mortar and pestle or some other way to mash it up without losing any of the powder. Mix the powder with a good-tasting liquid such as broth, or some yogurt, or a puree like baby food. Suck it up in the syringe and administer to the dog.

As with the meatball method, frequently administering syringes of yummy stuff without pills will help keep the method effective.

Teaching a Dog to Take a Pill

All of the methods above depend on disguise and deception. However, you can train dogs to take pills plain, just as you would train any other behavior. Again, if your dog has moderate to advanced dementia, she is not likely to be able to learn a behavior like this. But you may have or plan to get a younger dog. You can get an earlier start next time.

Laura VanArendonk Baugh of Canines In Action has a lovely method for teaching a dog to take pills and describes it in a blog post: "An Easy Pill To Swallow: Training to Take Pills the Easy Way" (see dogdementia.com/linklist).

I hope the ideas and products in this chapter can help you meet your dog's special needs in ways that minimize the difficulties for you. The next chapter has a bit more information on getting organized to help your dog, and then we're going to talk about *your* new needs.

References

Bayles, Kathryn A., and Cheryl K. Tomoeda. 2013. *MCI and Alzheimer's Dementia: Clinical Essentials for Assessment and Treatment of Cognitive-Communication Disorders.* San Diego, CA: Plural Publishing.

Campbell, Sharon, Amy Trettien, and Brenda Kozan. 2001. "A Noncomparative Open-Label Study Evaluating the Effect of Selegiline Hydrochloride in a Clinical Setting." *Veterinary Therapeutics: Research In Applied Veterinary Medicine* 2 (1): 24-39.

Lavond, David G. and Joseph E. Steinmetz. 2003. *Handbook of Classical Conditioning.* Boston: Kluwer Academic Publishers.

[6]

Supplies

As our dogs get older, they need more care from us. This is especially true of dogs who are losing cognitive abilities. In chapters 4 and 5, I discussed some of the ways we can help our old dogs with purchased products.

Below are more concise lists of supplies that I and other caretakers of dogs with dementia have found helpful. It bears repeating: if using a product entails learning a skill, it's probably not practical for your dog with dementia.

For Elimination Problems

- Plastic bags
- Paper towels
- Diapers
- Antidiarrheal medication (if approved by vet)
- Canned pumpkin puree (can be helpful for both diarrhea and constipation)
- Washable bedding
- Latex or plastic disposable gloves
- Enzyme cleaner
- Baby or pet wipes

- A plastic tub (for a partial bath, e.g., if your dog has stepped in poop)
- Bath towels

For Eating and Drinking Problems

- Elevated food bowls (not recommended for breeds prone to bloat; see the list on page 62)
- Food-grade squeeze tubes
- Syringes (without needles)
- Baby food
- Elevated water dish with tank (not recommended for breeds prone to bloat)

For Mobility Problems

- Foam-backed bath mats
- Rubber shower mats
- Textured treads for smooth floors
- Dog boots
- Traction socks
- Toenail covers
- Ice carpets
- Lift harnesses
- Slings
- Strollers
- Lifts (doggie elevators for stairs)

For Dogs Who Wander

- Baby gates
- Exercise pens
- Edge and corner guards
- Cable conduit and cord covers
- Ramps (only if the dog can't get hurt falling off)

- Indoor and outdoor night-lights
- Motion-sensitive lights

How to Choose a Dog Bed

Rather than list specific types of beds, I'll mention here the issues to consider when choosing a bed for your dog with dementia:

- Can he get in it safely? Your dog may be losing the ability to make decisions about taking a nap or getting into bed. He may not even be able to find his bed. So you need a bed that's low to the ground for that dog and a big enough target for him to find or stumble over. I've mentioned that I put a donut bed in the middle of Cricket's safe room when she had advanced dementia and lost the ability to go to bed on her own. She would literally stumble over it, fall in, then go to sleep. You may want multiple beds, perhaps in corners where the dog tends to get stuck or areas where he commonly wanders.

Cricket tripping into bed

- Can he get out of it safely? The bed itself shouldn't be able to slide around, and the dog may need extra traction when he gets out, so if you have slick floors, put the bed on a rubber or foam-backed mat and surround it with more as needed, in any direction he may exit. These can also help prevent him from hurting himself if he stumbles on the way out of bed.

- Is the firmness appropriate? Memory foam beds are now available for pets, and many older dogs or dogs with joint stiffness seem to find them comfortable. But the firmness will also affect how easy it is for your dog to get out of bed. This is something you may need to experiment with to find the best fit.

- Will other dogs contest him for it? I've written already about the need to give your dog with dementia a safe place. If your dog does stay regularly with another dog or two who might hog the bed, get as many of the preferred beds as you have dogs. Plus one more if you can afford it.

- Does he need extra help to stay warm? Many small dogs love getting under covers and develop skills for burrowing. There are even little sleeping bags for dogs now. But a dog with dementia may lose the ability to take action to get warm or to get back out from under covers. My little Cricket stopped getting under the covers for the last year or so of her life, and that was probably just as well. She couldn't navigate well under the best of conditions, and would likely have been very confused under sheets and a blanket in the dark. There are heated dog beds now, as well as free-standing heaters that might be appropriate. I was too worried about the risks of fire and electric shock to use either, although many have good safety features. Instead, I gently covered Cricket with a light blanket when it was chilly. Some dogs can safely wear a loose-fitting nightshirt as well. I also used a hot water bottle, wrapped in a towel, and some microwavable pillows filled with rice that can hold the heat for a couple hours. Just be sure you don't get them too hot initially.

[7]

How to Help Yourself

Many challenges come with caring for a dog with dementia. We need to cope emotionally with the decline of our dog's cognition and capabilities. We need to change our own behavior, which can be difficult. The orderliness of our household may be affected. We may feel lonely and overburdened.

Just as in any other caregiving situation, we need to find ways to help ourselves as well as our charges.

Empathy Gone Wild: Coping with the Sorrow

You love your dog, or you wouldn't have this book. It's hard on anyone to see a beloved companion lose capabilities with age. And as hard as it is to accept the effects of arthritis or cataracts, it can be even more difficult to witness the signs of cognitive decline.

But the thing is, your dog probably doesn't know what she is losing. Many humans with Alzheimer's or other dementia conditions don't. Unawareness of one's own cognitive deficits (anosognosia) is common among people with Alzheimer's and is considered a symptom of the disease (Lopez et al 1994).

We are only now learning about dogs' cognitive abilities. As intelligent as they may be, our canine friends probably can't look at their own internal mental processes in an analytical way. They probably do not experience regret for lost skills or frustration with memory problems (Horowitz 2010, 222-228). In many situations, we admire their ability to "be in the moment." In the case of dementia, it can be a saving grace. You remember who they once were, but they probably don't.

We shouldn't assume our dogs are necessarily suffering because their behavior is becoming odd. For example, you see your dog wandering in circles. This is distressing to you. But is the dog distressed? She may be, or she may be perfectly fine with it. The wandering may be beneficial because she is getting moderate exercise and encountering the nice, smelly kibble you scattered for her to sniff out on the rug, rather than lying on a couch all day. On the other hand, the repetitive movement may be causing strain on her joints and muscles, or the constant turning in one direction may be harmful to the vertebrae in her neck or back.

You need to go beyond the initial emotional reaction and really observe your dog. My little Cricket tended to walk in large counterclockwise circles, and her body was not tense or strained. But I have seen videos of dogs with dementia who turned such tight circles that they were essentially twirling slowly in place, and I worried about the health and happiness of those dogs. Even then, though, I didn't know them and was in no position to judge.

A consult with a vet is essential. We associate certain behaviors with suffering in our minds, but the suffering may or may not be there. Dementia is a foreign condition to many of us, one that forces us to drop some assumptions. A vet can assess whether the behavior is causing physical pain or deterioration and help you monitor its effect on your dog's quality of life.

This chapter is about you, the human. But the best thing I did for myself, as Cricket's human, was to make an effort to see her for who she was in that moment—to focus on the dog in front of me, not the dog I remembered.

Learning About Human Dementia

As well as having a dog with dementia, I had the interesting, sometimes painful experience of having a human family member diagnosed with Alzheimer's. I noticed similarities in caring for them, and several people who have contacted me through my website have mentioned this as well. Since there are few resources about the experience of taking care of a dog with dementia, a window into the life of a caregiver for a human with dementia might be helpful.

Blogs About Caregiving

Lists of well regarded blogs on dementia caregiving can be found in these online articles:

- Healthline: "The Best Alzheimer's Blogs of the Year"
- Ezra Home Care: "The Five Best Blogs About Alzheimer's and Dementia"

(See dogdementia.com/linklist for links to both.)

Books About Caregiving

There are dozens of good books on Alzheimer's caregiving. These are my favorites:

- Joanne Koenig Coste, *Learning to Speak Alzheimer's: A Groundbreaking Approach for Everyone Dealing with the Disease*

- Gary LeBlanc, *Staying Afloat in a Sea of Forgetfulness: Common Sense Caregiving*

Most books about Alzheimer's and other dementia conditions in humans are written for caregivers. And they do need support: more than a third of dementia caregivers report symptoms of depression.

However, the number of publications by people with dementia is also growing. I think these first-person accounts are also valuable to read. Here are a few:

Blogs by People with Dementia

- *Which Me Am I Today?*
- *Sharing My Life with Lewy Body Dementia*

(See dogdementia.com/linklist for links to both.)

Books by People with Dementia

- Greg O'Brien, *On Pluto: Inside the Mind of Alzheimer's*
- Thomas DeBaggio, *Losing My Mind: An Intimate Look at Life with Alzheimer's*
- Richard Taylor, PhD, *Alzheimer's from the Inside Out*

Staying Organized

Your dog with dementia will need more of your time. Think of the needs your puppy had. He was completely dependent on you. You had to feed him frequently, make sure he was getting enough liquids, take him out to potty, direct him to the right things to chew, and spend lots of time teaching him how to be a happy family member. You won't be teaching your old doggie many new things after he has advanced dementia, but he is going to need a lot of personal care and guidance from you again.

Can you make a "supply station" for easy access to the things you need for cleanup? (Check the list in chapter 6.) If you live with others, can you organize a system for who's "on duty" to watch and help your old dog or take him out to eliminate every couple hours? If he's a particular eater, can you stock up on what he likes?

If you are taking care of him by yourself, or if you get complete buy-in from other family members, you can keep a chart. Track things like urination, defecation, meals and snacks, medication (especially if he takes any medications for which the dose might vary), and exercise. Leave a column for general comments about how he is doing that day. See the section on record keeping below.

Finding Community

So far the online communities I know of for people whose dogs have dementia are small. They include a Facebook group, the Canine Cognitive Dysfunction (CCD) Support Group; a Yahoo group that appears currently inactive, Canine Cognitive Dysfunction Syndrome; and my website, Dog Dementia: Help and Support. (See dogdementia.com/linklist for links to these.)

Dementia often hits when the dog is old enough to have several other health problems, some of which can mask cognitive decline. So owners often don't realize their dog has dementia until it's advanced. The people who comment on my website and write me personal emails are almost always struggling with the same question: should they euthanize their dog?

I can't determine whether this means they all have dogs with advanced dementia or they're all assuming that dementia is a death sentence. For many afflicted dogs, it is not. We tend to overreact to the unfamiliar, and also make assumptions about the dog's emotional state or comfort level.

This is the kind of situation where the support of a community can be really helpful.

I hope people with dogs who are still living with dementia can form more extensive support communities, online or in person, to help one another and exchange reliable information. As people get more familiar with this disease, perhaps individual pet owners will become aware of possible symptoms earlier and be able to perform more proactive interventions.

Seeking Respite Care

Sometimes the thing you need most in the world is a little break. Respite care is a concept borrowed from the human caregiving communities, wherein a loved one is cared for by a professional caregiver or another family member, sometimes outside the home, for a period of time.

I'm absolutely not recommending that you run out and put your elderly, cognitively impaired dog in daycare. Most would not be safe or happy in that situation, with the possible exception of those dogs who have gone to one regularly for their whole lives.

But if your dog still enjoys a ride in the car, or can feel and be safe in a friend's home, or can safely be left with a sitter at your home, you can get a break and maybe even provide your dog with some "Big Adventure Time" as discussed in the Enrichment section of chapter 4. Don't be embarrassed that you want to get away sometimes. If you can do it without your dear dog getting too anxious, I encourage you to take any opportunity that is safe.

Getting Enough Sleep

Some of the most difficult situations I know of involve dogs who wander and vocalize at night. Some of these dogs are still quite capable in other ways, enjoying life during the day and interacting with their people. But they roam the house at night, sounding miserable and keeping people awake.

Crating the dog can help with the wandering if he is generally happy in a crate, but he may still vocalize if awake. A reader of my website, Judith Collins, resolved her dog's night wandering and barking by installing solar-powered lights by his bed. It turned out that his agitation was a result of getting lost in the dark.

Another option is to check with your veterinarian about safe sedation for the dog (and please check with your vet regarding not just prescription drugs but also the safety and effectiveness of any supplements you're thinking of using). But even medication does not always work, or may not be safe for a frail dog. In that case you will need to catch sleep when you can. You may be able to use earplugs or white noise to mask the worst of the sound, if you are sure you can hear what you need to for safety. There is not always an easy fix for this.

Keeping Records and Notes

The benefits of keeping records of our dogs' lives extend well beyond being able to refer to them at vet visits. Humans are notoriously bad at assessing the dates of events (Hammond 2012), and the kinds of gradual changes that are connected to a long-term condition may be the hardest of all to track.

You will need to make decisions on behalf of your dog, and the more information you have, the better decisions you can make. Keeping records and notes can be especially helpful if you need to face the hard question of whether to euthanize your dog. With records, you will have reliable points of comparison with which to assess the quality of her life.

I wish I had logged more information. When did Cricket first start having GI problems? Did they get worse over time or did I just think they did? When did the rear-end weakness start? When did she stop being friendly to one of her best human friends?

I wish I had written a short monthly assessment of what Cricket could do and not do, her general mood, and what physical problems she had. A monthly video of her doing her normal activities would have been very helpful as well. The videos and photos I did take show some of the changes in her capabilities over time, but I was not methodical about it.

We forget. For instance, in the summer of 2012, I wrote the following in an email to a friend:

> Cricket is stiff in the morning and a little slow to get going mentally. But she notably perks up as the day progresses. When I first take her out the door, without fail she takes a deep breath, then snorts. I set her down and hold her steady while she tries out her legs, and soon she is toddling around, checking out what smells are new since she was out last. A little bit later, she is downright frisky. She often follows me, hopping up and down, as I prepare and serve her breakfast. And by the time I leave for work, she is generally crowding me at the door to make sure that I don't forget to take her along.

When I reread that nine months later, I was jolted into awareness of the capabilities Cricket had lost since then. She didn't really follow scents anymore, and she had forgotten the work routine, even though I took her with me most days. But she remained interested in smells, enjoying them in a less purposeful way, and she still hopped a tiny bit for her meals.

Documentation can serve an emotional purpose too. I got Cricket in 2002, several years before I had a smartphone or video camera. I got a video camera in late 2008, which means that in my earliest videos of her she is already 12 years old. It is hard to remember her younger years now, when she was so active and athletic. I am grateful for the videos I made, but I wish I had some earlier ones.

You may have the capabilities to take videos now. If you haven't already, start filming your old dog now, both to keep a record of her capabilities and to enjoy later. I bet you'll be glad you did.

Planning for the Future

This is hard to think about, but how would your dog cope if something happened to you?

For the last year of Cricket's life, a dear friend had instructions from me to euthanize her if I were to pass away first. This was not some ego trip on my part. I was Cricket's only anchor in life. She would not be able to transfer her trust and comfort to another person and would not be able to cope at all in a new environment. I did not want my friend to have to agonize over the decision, and I didn't want Cricket to suffer.

This decision will be different for everybody. Many people and their dogs have larger families or close circles of friends with whom the old dog is still comfortable. But whatever your situation, for the sake of your dog and human loved ones, make your wishes known and write them down. You can even create a pet trust or a codicil in your will. Talk to a lawyer or find an online template to use. Your dog is a treasured family member, and you can take steps to ensure that he or she is cared for appropriately.

References

Hammond, Claudia. 2012. *Time Warped: Unlocking the Mysteries of Time Perception*. Edinburgh: Canongate.

Horowitz, Alexandra. 2010. *Inside of a Dog: What Dogs See, Smell, and Know*. New York: Scribner.

Lopez, Oscar L., James T. Becker, Denise Somsak, Mary Amanda Dew, and Steven T. DeKosky. 1994. "Awareness of Cognitive Deficits and Anosognosia in Probable Alzheimer's Disease." *European Neurology* 34 (5): 277-282

[8]

Quality-of-Life Considerations

There are some situations that can make it more difficult to care for dogs with dementia. Other illnesses, pain, and even size can affect our ability to keep them safe and comfortable. This chapter offers information—and moral support—regarding these special situations.

Concurrent Diagnoses

The health problems experienced by most older dogs can make both the diagnosis and the treatment of canine cognitive dysfunction difficult. And an additional medical condition, however slight, can make life with CCD very difficult for the dog.

Other conditions may mask CCD's symptoms. If your dog is losing his sight, you may attribute his standing at the wrong side of the door to that. If his hearing is failing, you may think that's why he seems less responsive to you and is starting to live in his own little world. If he has arthritis in his hips, you may attribute mild circling behavior to an asymmetry in his joint problems.

Almost every symptom of dementia can also be caused by a different medical condition. And it works the other way as well. You may think your dog has dementia, but he might have another medical condition, even including a different mental illness.

Assuming your dog is properly diagnosed, there can be problems with treating him for CCD. The principal drug prescribed in the U.S. for CCD, selegiline, can not be safely taken with certain other mental health drugs, including tricyclic antidepressants like amitriptyline or SSRIs like fluoxetine (Landsberg et al 2008). Even choosing a dietary approach can be difficult if the dog has food allergies or sensitivities.

Finally, canine cognitive dysfunction can intensify the severity of other conditions, including those that would otherwise be trivial. When Cricket was about 15 years old, her hind legs started to weaken and would collapse under her sometimes. I had to hold her up to potty. I was afraid she was in pain, and was planning a vet visit when a joint on one of her front legs also stopped working and she started to limp. I thought: *This is it.* No way could she cope with a bad front leg and two weak hind legs. Even if we could get the pain or stiffness controlled, I didn't think she would be able to figure out how to walk.

But by the time we got to the vet, she had full use of her front leg again. It may have been a temporary circulatory or nerve problem. I had the vet assess the function of her rear legs and give an opinion as to whether Cricket was in pain. She said that Cricket had neurological weakness in her hind legs but that it was not a painful condition and that Cricket did not appear to be in pain. Nor was it an advanced case. Cricket was already on a light dose of a nonsteroidal anti-inflammatory medication for her joints, and the vet didn't even see any need to raise it. I felt like we'd dodged a bullet.

But later we had another close call. I came home one day to find that Cricket had scratched her cornea, as she had done many times throughout her life with me. She normally got medication for it, then had to wear a plastic cone to prevent her from bothering it until it healed.

Over time, she had spent many months wearing a cone and had become accustomed to it. But it was a different story when she was 15. Her walking was already wobbly

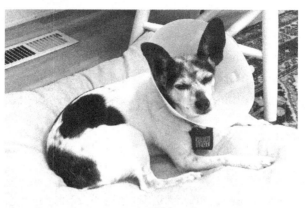

Cricket in the days of the plastic cone

from the rear-end weakness, and she got stuck in corners. I didn't think she'd be able to cope with a cone. I feared she

Cricket's soft protective collar

would injure herself if she wore one, and that the eye would never heal if she didn't. I came home from the vet that day crying, actually considering the possibility of euthanizing her because of an eye scratch.

Then I found out about some alternatives to plastic cones— collars that are like donut-shaped pillows that go around the dog's neck. I found one in a local store, and—voila!—problem solved. Cricket could walk without bashing into things with a cone. Her eye healed up in less than a week, and she lived more than a year longer.

For a dog who can barely learn anything, what might normally be only a moderate physical problem can be very serious. Don't underestimate your dog's quality of life with dementia. But also don't overestimate her ability to cope with new things, including changes in her health and physical capabilities.

Pain

Identifying Pain

Pain is one of the biggest quality-of-life issues for our dogs, but we may have difficulty telling when they actually hurt. So our first task in keeping our dogs free from pain, or at least at a livable level of discomfort, is to learn to detect it.

Some signs are straightforward. If your dog starts limping or greatly favoring a limb, she is very likely in pain. Back pain often manifests itself in extreme stiffness and an odd body carriage, including but not limited to an arched or roached back. If your dog is reluctant to get up from lying down, or to sit or lie down from standing, pain is a possibility. With conditions like arthritis, it can be hard to distinguish between pain and stiffness. (And moderate-to-extreme stiffness is also a quality-of-life issue.)

Some signs of pain are less obvious to us. Dogs lick themselves for myriad reasons, including grooming, boredom, or itching. But excessive licking of one area can also indicate pain.

Building muscle in one part of the body can mean that the dog is avoiding use of another. This typically happens with pain in the lower back or hind legs; muscle is built in the neck and shoulders.

If she keeps her tail tucked, she might be hurting.

Other signs of extreme pain can be trembling, agitation, or inexplicable panting, i.e., panting not tied to recent exertion or heat.

Frequent stretching can also indicate pain. This is a hard one to see, since stretching looks charming and pleasant, and most dogs stretch a couple times a day. Watch out for changes in frequency.

Any of the above should prompt a visit to your veterinarian regardless of the dog's age. But regular checkups are key too, as they can put your dog in front of an expert who can catch pain earlier.

Vaccines, the main reason most people see a vet with any regularity, are no longer required every year in parts of the U.S. and other countries, and so many of us are taking our pets to the vet less frequently. But our senior animals not only need regular wellness exams, they probably need them even more than younger animals. The American Animal Hospital Association (AAHA) recommends checkups every six months for senior dogs (Epstein 2005, 82), which it defines as those in the last 25 percent of their projected life span (see dogdementia.com/linklist). Older dogs are more likely to be on medications that need monitoring and are more vulnerable to illness, disease, and pain (not to mention cognitive dysfunction).

So get your dog in front of a vet both on schedule and when there is any change. None of us wants our best friend to be secretly suffering.

Treating Pain

The two main types of prescription medications for chronic pain are nonsteroidal anti-inflammatories and steroids. They are almost never prescribed together, nor should two of either type be combined. The following is general information about the two types, including side effects.

NSAIDs

Nonsteroidal anti-inflammatories (NSAIDs) exist for dogs as well as humans. But they are not the same. Do not administer human pain medications to your dog.

The most commonly prescribed NSAID for aches and pains in dogs is carprofen, which is sold under many names, including Rimadyl (most common in the U.S.), Vetprofen, Novox, Imadyl, Imafen, Rovera, Norocarp, Tergive, Carprodyl, and Carprobay.

When carprofen was first introduced in the U.S., under the brand name Rimadyl in 1997, it was heavily marketed and hailed as a wonder drug. But it turns out carprofen can have serious side effects, especially for dogs who have gastrointestinal issues (it can cause ulceration and bleeding), kidney problems, or liver problems (Mansa et al 2007). A considerable number of dog deaths have been attributed to its use, and even though these side effects are common to all NSAIDs (Lascelles et al 2007), multiple lawsuits have been filed against Pfizer, the manufacturer of Rimadyl. A web search on the brand name Rimadyl will yield many sites that go so far as to call it poison.

On the other hand, numerous studies have found it to be both effective and safe. Most of the known side effects can be identified quickly if they do occur.

A large study (805 dogs) in 2007 yielded information on both efficacy and side effects of treatment for osteoarthritis with carprofen (Mansa et al. 2007). At the end of the study, 26.7 percent of the dogs were no longer lame, and another 49.2 percent had improved. The duration of lameness prior to the study was recorded for 290 dogs. A significantly higher percentage of the dogs with lameness for under six months showed improvement.

(This points to the value of early intervention in pain and stiffness from arthritis.)

Twenty-four dogs, about 3 percent, were removed from the study because of side effects—generally diarrhea and/or vomiting. Two dogs were diagnosed with liver dysfunction. One had a mild case and recovered soon after the administration of carprofen was stopped. The other dog had a more serious case that required medical intervention. That dog also survived (and is the dog mentioned below as the only dog to suffer a serious reaction out of more than 1,500 from combined studies of carprofen).

In 2010, researchers reviewed 15 studies of carprofen and other NSAIDs (firocoxib, etodolac, meloxicam, aspirin, deracoxib, and licofelone) to determine whether long-term use of NSAIDs had higher risks (Innes, Clayton, and Lascelles 2010). The studies had been published between 1999 and 2007. Five of them were solely about carprofen, and five others compared carprofen to another drug. A total of 1,589 dogs were included.

Fourteen of the 15 papers reported on the safety of NSAID use. The average experimental adverse event rate from these was 11 percent—meaning that a possible negative side effect was reported in 11 percent of the dogs administered NSAIDs in all the studies. Only one study included a control group (a group that did not receive the drug), but in that study the control group had an even higher reported adverse event rate (Raekallio et al. 2006).

The review paper notes:

> Only one adverse event, which was probably linked to treatment and considered serious, was reported in all the papers reviewed. This was a labrador with an episode of toxic idiosyncratic hepatitis; the dog was treated and survived (Innes, Clayton, and Lascelles 2010, 229).

In addition, the major conclusion of the paper was that long-term use (exceeding 28 days) of NSAIDs in dogs did not present more risk than short-term use.

Today carprofen is prescribed with a mandatory disclosure of side effects. Educated vets prescribe the lowest effective dose, monitor the dog after prescribing, and most important, perform blood work before using it, especially on older dogs, to check the baseline health of the dog's liver and kidneys. The vet can also check for drug interactions. Carprofen is contraindicated, according to the manufacturer, for use in combination with some other drugs, mainly other NSAIDs and corticosteroids.

Many dog owners are extremely wary of the side effects of drugs. It is human nature to focus on the possibility of dramatic adverse events even when the likelihood is very small (Kahneman 2011, 300-309). Many of us are fiercely protective of our dogs and do not want to take any risks with their care. But NSAIDs have been tested and shown to help, as opposed to many alternative remedies that have not. The lack of rigorous testing in alternative medicine also means there can be unknown side effects.

There appears to be a small risk of negative side effects in dogs taking carprofen or other NSAIDs. Meanwhile, there is a very large risk of the dog remaining in pain if he is not treated at all or treated ineffectively.

Steroids

The other medications commonly prescribed for pain are anti-inflammatory steroids. Steroids commonly used in veterinary care include prednisone, methylprednisolone, prednisolone, cortisone, fludrocortisone, isoflupredone, triamcinolone, dexamethasone, betamethasone, and flumethasone. (All of the medical information about steroids in this section comes from the online Merck Veterinary Manual, which is linked at dogdementia.com/linklist.)

Interestingly, steroids seem less controversial than NSAIDs, even though they are known to have numerous side effects. There is a fair amount of public awareness of these side effects, and veterinarians tend to be well versed in them. When steroids are administered, the goal is generally to use the lowest effective dose possible over the shortest period of time.

It's tempting to use steroids as a panacea, because they do tend to make animals (including humans) feel better very quickly. They can offer swift relief from pain, swelling, itching, and some gastrointestinal maladies.

One of the short-term side effects of steroid use is an almost immediate increase in hunger and thirst, and as a result, increased elimination. The first day one of my dogs got a fast-acting steroid, I left him in my bedroom as usual and went to work. When I got home, four hours later, this beautifully house-trained little dog had drained his water bowl, gone to sleep on my bed pillow, and completely voided his bladder.

Other common short-term effects are panting and mood changes, including depression and anxiety. These can lead to behavior changes ranging from lethargy to hyperactivity to aggression.

The side effects of long-term steroid use can be serious. Steroids tend to suppress the immune system, slowing healing and making the animal more prone to bacterial and fungal infections. The animal gains weight easily if allowed to overeat, but also from fluid retention. Steroids can facilitate urinary tract infections that do not manifest in all the usual symptoms and are harder to diagnose. The animal can suffer from muscle weakness and thinning of the skin. Steroids can also trigger diabetes or Cushing's disease, another serious endocrine disorder.

Hence, after a dog has been on steroids for more than two or three months, it is appropriate to reassess the need. The health costs and benefits must be regularly weighed. And a dog who is on a long-term or permanent course of steroids should be evaluated regularly by a vet, with blood work and urinalysis.

There are other prescription painkillers used for pain in dogs, especially acute pain, as from an injury or after surgery. Some of these, such as gabapentin and tramadol, are used for long-term pain as well.

This overview is intended to familiarize you with common painkillers and their pros and cons. It's not comprehensive and should not be interpreted as medical advice. Rather, I hope it will help you formulate questions to ask your vet when you speak to her about your dog's possible pain.

Online Resources on Pain and Pain Medications

These resources can be accessed at dogdementia.com/linklist.

- The American Animal Hospital Association's handout: "15 Signs of Pain in Dogs"
- An FDA document: "Get the Facts About Pain Relievers for Pets" (overview of NSAIDs)
- "Rimadyl: Friend or Foe," certified animal behavior consultant Steve Dale's four-part series about the introduction of Rimadyl and the ensuing controversy

Special Considerations for Large Dogs

All dog breeds appear to be equally susceptible to canine cognitive dysfunction. The source of this information is a study (Salvin et al. 2010, 280) that included a survey returned by almost 1,000 dog owners with dogs aged eight years or older. The requirement to take the survey was to own an "old dog," not necessarily to have a dog diagnosed with dementia.

For the purposes of statistical analysis, the dogs were split by breed into three groups: short lived, average, and long lived. When the incidence of canine cognitive dysfunction in these groups was computed, it was found to be equal. But as you might guess, for giant-breed dogs and other short-lived breeds, signs of cognitive dysfunction tended to show up at an earlier age.

Having a dog with cognitive dysfunction is likely to be harder in every way for owners of large dogs than it is for those with small or medium-size dogs. Smaller dogs are easier to physically assist, more easily controlled, and make smaller messes. I could pick up Cricket when she was headed the wrong direction, and when she forgot how to use the stairs, I carried her. It was easy to make her a safe space that she couldn't climb, chew, or push her way out of. When she got poop embedded between her toes, I could plunk her in a basin to wash her feet. When she voided her bladder on a rug or in the bed, it soaked only a small area. Some of these tasks that were difficult or unpleasant for me might not even be possible for the owners of a large dog.

Chapter 5 includes items that make it easier to help a big dog with cognitive or physical limitations. But mostly I want to say to large dog owners that I know you have some tough decisions to make. Putting it bluntly, you may have to consider euthanizing your dog sooner in the progression of the illness than someone with a smaller dog would. And I hope from the bottom of my heart that you can feel OK about that. You will still decide according to the quality of your dog's life.

References

Epstein, Mark, Ned F. Kuehn, Gary Landsberg, B. Duncan X. Lascelles, Steven L. Marks, Jean M. Schaedler, and Helen Tuzio.
2005. "AAHA Senior Care Guidelines for Dogs and Cats." *Journal
of the American Animal Hospital Association* 41 (2): 81-91.

Innes, John F., J. Clayton, and B. Duncan X. Lascelles. 2010. "Review
of the Safety and Efficacy of Long-Term NSAID Use in the
Treatment of Canine Osteoarthritis." *The Veterinary Record* 166
(8): 226.

Kahneman, Daniel. 2011. *Thinking, Fast and Slow.* New York: Farrar,
Straus and Giroux.

Landsberg, Gary, Amanda Florsheim, Valerie Dramard, Teodoro Bottiglieri, and David Mischoulon. 2008. "S-adenosylmethionine
(SAMe) and cognitive dysfunction in dogs (Sponsored by Virbac
Animal Health): A Roundtable Discussion." DVM360.com. (See
dogdementia.com/linklist.)

Lascelles, B. Duncan X., J. Michael McFarland, and Heather Swann.
2005. "Guidelines for Safe and Effective Use of NSAIDs in Dogs."
Veterinary Therapeutics 6 (3): 237.

Salvin, Hannah E., Paul D. McGreevy, Perminder S. Sachdev, and
Michael J. Valenzuela. 2010. "Under Diagnosis of Canine Cognitive
Dysfunction: A Cross-Sectional Survey of Older Companion Dogs."
The Veterinary Journal 184 (3): 277-281.

[9]

Is the End Near?

Wouldn't it be nice to know the future? Will my beloved dog die a quiet, painless natural death at home? Will some traumatic health event force me to make a difficult and too-fast decision? Will I need to make a more considered decision at some point as I watch my dog slowly decline?

When to euthanize a beloved dog is a choice that many of us try to make with our heads, but sometimes our hearts don't cooperate. We never want to let go of our dog friends, and we agonize over whether we are making the right decisions for them. We wonder whether we are keeping them too long for our own comfort, at the expense of theirs. Or we are afraid we are ending their lives too soon.

The majority of emails and comments I get through my website are from people who are struggling with the question of whether to euthanize a dog with dementia. Considering euthanasia for a pet who is physically failing is difficult enough. But deciding that a dog who is still physically robust should depart this life is a new and awful experience for many of us.

One of my purposes in writing this book is to let people know that canine cognitive dysfunction is a disease. It is progressive and disabling. There are ways we can sometimes slow the pro-gression, and there are ways to help our dogs continue to experi-ence happiness. But nothing stops the disease, and there may be a point where your dog's life is no longer, on balance, a happy one. I believe that in these cases, euthanasia is not only defensi-ble but a blessing for the dog. So many people express such guilt and regret when they write to me about it. I can tell that they love and care for their dogs, and that their agony over the question of euthanasia is real and terrible. I want to reassure those people, and anyone caught in this decision-making process, that it is not inherently selfish to euthanize a dog who is suffering because of cognitive decline.

There are people who do not consider euthanizing a pet to be an option. There are ethical arguments against it; if there were not, the decision would not be so difficult. So I also respect those who do not support euthanasia. I am certain they love their dogs equally well. I hope those people will find the other resources in this book helpful.

In this chapter, I present some resources on analytical methods for assessing our pets' lives. These can be extremely helpful in raising awareness of various issues, even if we don't use them as strict guides. I also include writings from people who have made the difficult decision and were willing to share their thoughts, as well as my own story of Cricket's last days and how I made the hard decision to euthanize her. Finally, I talk about the process of euthanasia: the options available, how to plan for it, and what to expect.

Resources for Making a Decision About Euthanasia

Villalobos Quality of Life Scale

The Villalobos Quality of Life Scale has seven categories in which you rank the quality of your pet's life (see dogdementia.com/linklist). You can then add up the points to get a numerical score. Even if you don't like making decisions based on numbers, checking the scale every month or week, or at whatever interval is appropriate for your pet, will help you see whether your pet's situation is declining.

Online Resources

The following are trustworthy resources about euthanasia and making the decision and are available at dogdementia.com/linklist.

- ASPCA, "End of Life Care." What to expect in your pet's final days and how best to help.
- Dr. Alice Villalobos, "Quality of Life Assessment." An article by Dr. Villalobos about her Quality of Life Scale.
- American Humane Society, "Euthanasia: Making the Decision." Frank discussion about considering euthanasia and a description of the procedure.
- Dusty Rainbolt, "Let's Talk: When Is It Time to Say Goodbye to Your Dog?" Commentary on the Villalobos scale and other issues.

A Helpful Book

The book *Facing Farewell: Making the Decision to Euthanize Your Pet*, by veterinarian Julie Reck, is a comprehensive guide. It helps you prepare for a discussion with your vet and describes the euthanasia process in detail. This book was a real comfort to me as I assessed and reassessed little Cricket's quality of life. It is available as a print book and an ebook.

Making Your Own Lists

After reading some of these resources, and perhaps even tallying up the points on the Villalobos scale, you can make your own lists of what is pleasant or enjoyable in your dog's life and what is unpleasant, frustrating, or painful.

Here are sample lists of pleasures and difficulties for a senior dog:

Pleasures in My Dog's Life

- Food/treats
- Play
- Companionship with other dogs
- Human companionship
- Petting
- Snuggling
- Going places in the car
- Going for walks
- Walking around the yard
- Playing with toys
- Chewing things
- Playing training games
- Swimming or playing in water
- Lying in the sun
- Sniffing things
- Relaxing

Difficulties in My Dog's Life

(Include the severity and frequency.)

- Arthritis (being treated but hard to assess pain level)

- Eye condition requiring drops (starting to struggle against application of drops)
- Allergies (OK right now)
- Hypothyroid (well controlled)
- Anxiety (comes and goes)
- Mobility issues (moderate)
- Vomiting (about twice a week)
- Toileting problems (daily)
- Difficulty drinking water (most of the time)
- Can't get out of bed and soils herself (a couple times a week)

Your lists will be individual to your dog and will change as your dog ages. We need to pay attention to the loss of pleasures and the onset or worsening of difficulties.

Three Personal Stories

Two generous friends have shared the processes they went through in deciding to euthanize their pets with dementia. My own story with Cricket follows.

Sue Matthews of Echo Bouvier Kennel (see dogdementia.com/linklist) has written a very nice piece about her own ways to assess when the "time has come." Her approach is different from many people's, but is both loving and sensible. I quote her here with permission:

> I struggled with euthanasia for a long time when the first dog of my adult life, an amazing springer spaniel who had raised my children and even toddled my oldest grandchildren when they started learning to walk, was obviously aging. I was concerned for Rusty's welfare and quality of life, and as much as I hated the reality of him eventually passing on, I realized that it would likely be my responsibility to choose his time. I started asking more

experienced dog friends about how they had made this difficult decision. Some clearly did not want to talk about it and just responded with "Oh your dog will tell you when it's time." This was not sufficient for me, and didn't seem necessarily to be true.

I persisted in posing the question to many, many people over several years. What struck me the most was that almost every person who actually would talk about it ended their stories with "I really wish I had not waited so long." I took that to heart and decided that for me, the most important issue in the decision was the dog's comfort, quality of life, and dignity, and that I needed to set my own personal sense of loss, grief, or reluctance to say good-bye aside, for the dog's benefit. As a result of all those conversations, I decided that I would rather choose to say good-bye to my dog even a week early, rather than a day late, if it meant my dog was less likely to suffer in any way.

By the time Rusty was 15, it was clear that he was having significant issues with senility. He would walk into a corner of the kitchen and not be able to figure out how to get out again. It was clear this was incredibly stressful for him, and he would bark, whine, and cry. I tried sitting with him to try and calm him down, but sometimes I had to sedate him to help him settle down again. It was heartbreaking. He had become incontinent as well, and we were able to deal with that, but when I saw how easily he was upset I knew it was time to help him find peace.

I chose a date a week in advance and let my children know so that they could make plans to spend some time with Rusty. My son took him out for burgers and fries and spent the day in a park they used to play together in. One daughter took him to the lovely setting where her senior pictures had been shot, with Rusty included in the photos. My youngest took him to the beach to walk on the sand for the last time and get ice cream at the Tillamook Cheese Factory, a favorite activity they had shared many times over the years. It still chokes me up to talk about Rusty, even after all these 20 years. His passing was peaceful, and for a long time his ashes were in my van because he always loved to go bye-bye.

There are more little boxes in the hutch these days along with Rusty, but I've followed the same philosophy since we said good-bye to him, and it's worked out well for our family. Over the years, I've added some additional criteria to my decision making. The things I consider vital to a dog's well-being are: he needs to be able to eat, drink, eliminate, not be in pain, and show some interest and contentment in his life. Certainly I am willing to help a sick dog out to potty if some short-term help is needed until he recovers. I'm happy to cook special meals for a dog who needs that, take extra care to make sure a dog is well hydrated, or provide appropriate pain medication for a period of time. But I am not willing to subject a geriatric dog to extraordinary measures when there is not a reasonable expectation that the dog will recover enough to be able to meet his own very basic needs to eat, drink, and go potty, or when my dog shows me that he has lost interest in life. My beloved dogs deserve their dignity, and I feel that it's my responsibility to protect it. Having this mental checklist has helped me make better decisions for my dogs, rather than dwelling on my own sense of loss when a difficult decision needs to be made.

Blanche Axton of Pugalug Pug Rescue (see dogdementia.com/linklist) has more experience with the issue than anyone should have to. She has allowed me to quote her wise views on the subject, excerpted from her essay "Dancing With Death."

> I spend a lot of time thinking about death and suffering. I've dealt with a lot of both in my social work career, and I have dealt with them a GREAT deal in my canine res-cuing work.
>
> I don't fear death. I don't see it as the enemy or the bad thing to be avoided. Suffering is what I fear. Suffering is my great enemy. And I won't berate the coming of death when it puts an end to suffering that cannot be managed or ended through medical or behavioural approaches. Being alive is not the same as living.
>
> I am always about quality of life. I don't believe that letting nature take its course is the way to go. Nature is bloody cruel. Letting a dog or cat just die from its injuries or illness may be "natural" (whatever that means), but it often is neither kind nor humane.
>
> I would always rather let them go a day too early than a minute too late. And, of course, my dogs almost always rally at the vets and look better while they are there, but I know that as soon as we return home—if I chicken out—I will see again the very

behaviours that worried me to begin with. And I keep in my mind this thought: "Yes, she can rally for an hour in a high-stress, high-excitement environment. It's the other 23 hours I have to worry about."

I will fight hard to save my dogs, but not against un-winnable odds, and I won't make them suffer needlessly so that I can have closure and clarity. There often isn't any closure or clarity with some of the old dogs who just start to fail. I've learned to live with it, but it's damned hard. I've been so blessed to have a vet who will help me think it through and take myself out of the equation.

In all good conscience, I can't wait for my animals to be so miserable that they are suffering badly. I try to step back and objectively evaluate their life and their enjoyment. When I let my Pomeranian, Lola, go, I spent a lot of time thinking about this topic. To see Lola hiding under furniture and not even acknowledging me was too much. There was no joy there in a dog that had lived so large. So yes, sometimes my animals aren't skin and bones and limp rags when I say good-bye. I don't want them to go that way and I don't want my last memory to be that. I want to know that I didn't make them hang on so that I could feel that no one would question me. Even so, I always, always feel a mixture of guilt and relief when I let one of them go. Did I try hard enough? Should I have waited? Would she have rallied?

Ego, pride, life for life's sake, and suffering. Those are the enemy. And the little cedar boxes on my shelf ... they are small reminders of this. They are containers that hold the physical remains of some very fine dogs and cats. There isn't a container big enough to hold the intangibles—the fun, the memories, the struggle, the joy.

And here's my own story. I have written about Cricket's frailty, and how close I thought I was to having to euthanize her more than a year before I actually did. During that final year, as her senses, cognition, joints, and nervous system slowly deteriorated, I did more and more for her, and continually worked out little methods to keep her going. I knew even a minor health problem could make her situation unlivable, since she could not really learn to cope with anything new.

Her quality of life in her final months was good but precarious. After she could no longer drink water, I paid even closer attention. I was waiting for an event, a turning point where I could perceive that her light was going out.

I made my list, as described above, and kept remaking it as time passed.

I constantly assessed her quality of life. With all this deterioration, what were her pleasures and how potent were they? Were there big downsides to her life: pain, frustration, sensory limitations? How did things balance out?

I asked close friends their opinions of Cricket's life, to be sure I was not just perceiving things through the lens of my great desire for her to stay with me. All agreed that although she was deteriorating more quickly towards the end, each of her last days was a good one.

Cricket's last day on this earth was Friday, May 31, 2013. I never knew her exact age, but she was coming up on her 17th "birthday" as the vet and I had determined it.

Her last week was a good one. We kept to our usual schedule. She went to work with me most days, ate well with a little help from me, and snuggled with me at night.

On her last day she went to work with me. In retrospect, I am so grateful for this. I am so glad that I was there for what subsequently happened, and that she wasn't alone.

In the mid-morning she stood near her food bowl, so I gave her about two-thirds of a jar of baby food and water. She enjoyed it. (I typically did frequent feedings throughout the day. I was proud that she was in the same healthy weight range she had been for our whole life together.)

About half an hour later I heard her throw up. She vomited a large amount, then fell down on her side and had a seizure. Ruth and I rushed to her. Ruth held her gently down so she couldn't hurt herself (she was close to my desk and could have hit her head) and I held paper towels under her as she voided her bladder. Then I took over holding her gently. Her tongue was purple.

Within two minutes she started trying to get up. I gently held her in a more upright position. She had aspirated vomit and made hiccuping and choking noises. I put a dog bed in my lap and held her in the bed. I cleaned her mouth and, as I had on the very first day of our life together, I wiped her butt. She continued to cough and sputter.

This was it. It was time. I decided quickly that I was not going to let her go through that again. She could have been alone when it happened. She could have knocked her head on something or gotten trapped somewhere when she fell. Most important, more seizures seemed likely.

Seizures are not the end of the world. I had a larger dog who had seizures from probable epilepsy for the last 18 months of his life. He was still strong, and medication helped. But with Cricket, I had been watching for the "last straw" for some time. It could instead have been an injury. It could have been the diagnosis of a disease that would make her uncomfortable. It could have been sudden weight loss. She was frail and any untoward health event could have tipped her quality-of-life balance into the red.

The seizure was the sign to me that the danger and discomfort in her life now outweighed her pleasures, or would very soon.

Ruth helped me make the appointment. We called the vet as soon as we could and got in that day. Cricket was uncomfortable. At work, I sat in an office chair and held her, still supported in the dog bed. She sputtered and coughed for the next hour and a half, but she was glad to be held. And I was so glad to hold her.

At the appointed time, we headed to the vet and were able to go straight into a room that had been reserved for us. Cricket was alert, and her body was strong. She didn't give me any "sign" that she was ready to go. In fact, she gave several signs that she was not. She was not pleased about being handled by the vet, and struggled against it. Then, after the completion of the injections, she just wouldn't go. She was no longer struggling, nor do I think she was in pain. But she stayed and stayed. She required six times the calculated dosage of euthanasia drugs for a dog her size before she would leave this world.

I had long suspected that her last day would go that way. I wanted it to be easy—an easy decision for me, but more impor-tant, an easy experience for her. It was neither. She was too tough, too tenacious, too full of life.

I want to note that Cricket did not seem to be impaired by the seizure. As far as I could tell, her capabilities were unaffected. The seizure by itself was not the reason I chose to say good-bye that day. She might have had a few more good days, or maybe even a week or a month. But with all the ways that she was already im-paired, I was not willing to gamble. I didn't believe she could go on much longer not knowing how to drink. I worried that if the demen-tia worsened any more, she wouldn't know me, and would lose her home base in the world. I made the decision with my head, not my heart.

I share this as one person's decision process. I think there are many valid ways to look at the difficult, sometimes awful questions that arise when our pets near the end of their lives. I have made different decisions with different animals.

With one of my cats, I chose not to intervene at all, and she died at home, crawling under my bed at the end. I took another cat to be euthanized the day she had a seizure and fell off a table. She had cancer that had likely metastasized to her brain. Her previous few days, though, had been incredibly sweet. She had been a feral cat, and in the last part of her life accepted me fully and sought me out frequently, seemingly to make up for all the time she had spent at arm's length. Her last months were so enriching for us both.

My other dear little rat terrier, Gabriel, had a chronic autoimmune condition for the last year of his life, but spared me the decision by having a pulmonary embolism at home, passing into a coma, and peacefully leaving this world before I could even decide whether to take him to the emergency vet.

I would love to say that Cricket somehow told me she was ready to go. But she didn't tell me that. I had to own my decision completely. It was up to me as her guardian to decide for her, and I still believe it was the right decision. If I had it to do over again, I would do it the same way. But I wouldn't be happy about it, just as I wasn't then.

Euthanasia: Before, During, and After

If your dog has dementia, you probably have some lead time to carefully consider what to do if you decide to euthanize your dog. These are some of the choices you'll need to make:

Where to Perform the Procedure

I don't know many people who would choose to take their dog to the vet to be euthanized if there were an option to do it at home. Many of our dogs are scared at the vet, and as a public place, it's not ideal for grieving. However, it is a medical facility, and has the appropriate setup, often with a vet who is acquainted with our dog.

The in-home option is still fairly rare. There is now a franchise business in the United States called Lap of Love Veterinary Hospice that specializes in in-home euthanasia. I haven't used it, but I like the idea very much and will be keeping it in mind. There's a website where you can check for a Lap of Love veterinarian in your area (see dogdementia.com/linklist).

If I were to consider the option of in-home euthanasia by a vet who didn't specialize in it, I would talk to her beforehand about what equipment and medications she normally brings. After it took six times the normal dosage to euthanize Cricket, I have wondered whether a vet on a home visit would have brought along that much medicine for a 12-pound dog.

The potential drawbacks of having the vet perform euthanasia at home are possible interruptions from family members or other pets and distress to family members who are not prepared. Most people will know whether these may be problems for their household.

Who Will Do What

At the very least, it's good to know who will handle the pet and who may be there to help, whether at a vet's office or at home. If you are going to a clinic, be sure you have a steady driver.

What to Do with the Remains

There are several options for respectful treatment of our dear pets' remains. Most vets in the United States work with a pet cremation service. These businesses usually offer either an individual cremation, after which you receive your pet's ashes, or a less expensive group cremation. When the individual cremation is chosen, most businesses return the ashes in an attractive carved box with the pet's name on it. (Both Sue Matthews and Blanche Axton refer above to having many of these boxes.) There are also businesses that will incorporate your pet's ashes into artwork or jewelry.

Some more urban areas have pet cemeteries. There may also be the option of burying your pet at home—but check local ordinances, especially if you live in a city.

I'll insert a caveat here for those who have never saved a pet's ashes before and are considering it. I had decided ahead of time to keep Cricket's ashes. I'm a potter, and I took several weeks to make an urn for them, a labor of love. I loved her so much, and I thought having her ashes would be a comfort. But for me, it was not. I'm not particularly squeamish, but I don't like the ashes. They aren't Cricket. She's still gone. Many, many people take comfort in keeping their pets' ashes, but it's not for everyone.

How to Help Your Other Animals

We don't know how much dogs understand about death, but many form close attachments to their family members and clearly miss human and animal friends when they are gone. When we have multiple animals in our household, most of us want a way to let the others know that one has passed. This can happen naturally if the dog dies at home or if her body returns home, but is more difficult if the dog is taken away to be euthanized, then cremated.

When Cricket was euthanized, I made sure that my hands were covered with her scent after she passed. I touched her face and body. (I would have anyway.) When I came home, I immediately let the other three dogs smell my hands. With dogs' outstanding olfactory powers, my guess is that they could detect the odor of death, even though Cricket had been dead for only a few minutes when I left the vet.

None of my dogs displayed a noticeable reaction, and I didn't expect it. Only one of them regularly spent any time with her, and they weren't close. What Cricket's death meant to my other dogs was more freedom of movement in the house and more of my time, so if they did understand, it was all fine with them, as far as I know.

Many people report emotional responses from their dogs when an animal they are close to passes away. Dr. Patricia McConnell describes one of her dogs pacing around the body of the deceased dog, and writes about dogs not eating or expressing distress in other ways when one of their close friends passes away. Dr. McConnell's blog post "Helping a Dog Through a Loss" is brilliant (see dogdementia.com/linklist).

Like people, animals have different responses to change in their lives. Most people find that offering their surviving pets extra attention and care will help them through hard times.

Grief Resources for Humans

The loss of a pet is coming to be acknowledged as a true loss, one that can be felt as intensely as the loss of a human family member. There are now some excellent resources to help people cope with this grief. All of the following are available at dogdementia.com/linklist.

Online

- Argus Institute at Colorado State
- Association for Pet Loss and Bereavement
- Lightning Strike Pet Loss Support
- Rainbow Bridge Grief Support Community (a for-profit site)
- Senior Dogs Photo Gallery (a page on the website that accompanies this book where you can submit a photo of your dog)

Telephone

These support hotlines for pet loss are generally answered only during set hours. You can call to find out the hours, and some offer the option of leaving a message so you can get a return call.

- Cornell University College of Veterinary Medicine: 607-253-3932

- Washington State University College of Veterinary Medicine: 509-335-5704 or plhl@vetmed.wsu.edu
- Chicago Veterinary Medical Association: 630-325-1600
- Tufts University: 508-839-7966

In most countries, if you need to talk to someone immediately, you can call a crisis or suicide-prevention hotline. In the United States you can call the National Crisis Hotline at 800-273-8255.

Beyond the Grief

My little Cricket has been gone about two years as of the writing of this book. She is still so present in my heart that the writing has been a bittersweet experience. I'm pleased that other people may read about her, see her in photos and videos, and come to know her in a small way. But nothing takes the place of having her here with me.

I learned so much from Cricket's dementia. I'm much better prepared now to care for a dog with marked cognitive decline. I have learned about many products that can help. I've learned tricks for certain problem behaviors, although I'm sure the next time I deal with this, the problems will be different.

Most important of the practical lessons are these:

- I can recognize the signs and progression of canine cognitive dysfunction.
- I have learned there are medical interventions that may slow it down.
- I have figured out some pretty good ways to help a dog with dementia.

Because of what I learned, I am preparing to take some preventive steps with my oldest dog, Summer, who'll be 10 years old soon. I don't know her life expectancy because she is a very mixed breed, unrecognizable as anything in particular. (Even her genetic testing was indeterminate.) She weighs about 30 pounds and seems in perfect health, except for a controlled thyroid problem. She is active and sharp, and has no aches or pains that I can detect.

But sometime in the next year, I'll talk to my vet about starting Summer on either a prescription drug or a supplement to support her cognition. I'm planning that because many of the studies found significant benefits in long-term administration of treatments. If the vet recommends it, I'm ready to give her a jump start in case it will help.

And back to my dear Cricket. I listed above some of the practical things I learned from her. But my heart learned something too. No matter what the disease did to her, she was still my dog. Even as her demeanor flattened and some of her little quirks fell by the wayside, I still saw little sparkles of Cricket peeking through every day. Maybe that's not true for all dogs. I know that we were fairly lucky. Perhaps a dog can live so long with cognitive decline that she is no longer "in there." But Cricket was always there.

I hope what I have shared in this book is helpful to you and your own dogs. I hope you can intervene in the progress of the disease if it's not too late, and if not, I hope you can help your dog to have many more comfortable, happy days with you.

Index

as enrichment, 55
as part of treatment, 34
tracking dog's behavior and
    status, 101.
    See also records, keeping
training. *See* also desensitization
    and counterconditioning
    Cricket's, 7
    forgetting, as symptom of
        CCD, 22
    studied as CCD treatment, 34
    taking a pill, 89
trapped, getting
    as hazard of CCD, 47
    as symptom of CCD, 22
treatments
    adrafinil, 31
    Aktivait, 37
    Anipryl, 28
    apoaequorin, 37
    controlling weight, 35
    enrichment, 33
    Hill's diet, 32
    Neutricks, 37
    nicergoline, 30
    phosphatidylserine, 37
    prescription drugs, 28
    propentofylline, 31
    Purina diet, 32
    SAMe, 36
    selegiline, 28
    Senilife, 37
    supplements, 35
    Vivitonin, 31
    weight control, 35
trembling
    as sign of pain, 111
    as symptom of CCD, 20
tucked tail, as sign of pain, 110

veterinarians
    consulting about drug
        interactions, 114
    consulting about pain, 98
    consulting about sedation for
        night wandering dog, 103
    consulting about
        supplements, 37, 103
    mobile, for euthanasia, 130
    necessary to diagnose CCD, 23
    seeing for wellness exams, 111
veterinary behaviorists, board
    certified, 39
videos
    to assess dog's stress, 78
    as memorabilia, 104
    for record keeping, 104
Villalobos Quality of Life Scale,
    121
vision loss, confused with CCD, 12

wandering problems
    locator collars or tags, 53
    motion detectors, 53
    supplies for, 92
    webcams, 52
water. *See* drinking
waterers, 61p
    to make drinking easier, 61
webcams, 52, 52p
wellness exams, 111
wheels for dogs, problems with,
    74
will, including your dog in, 105
withdrawing socially, as symptom
    of CCD, 18

yoga mats, for traction, 76

Zylkene, 38

About the Author

Eileen Anderson writes about learning theory, her life with three dogs, and training with positive reinforcement on her popular blog, *Eileen and Dogs,* and for other publications. She brings to bear on these subjects a science background, critical thinking skills, and teaching experience.

Eileen has worked professionally as a writer and academic editor, a network administrator, a remedial college math instructor, and a trainer of computer skills in academic and workplace settings. She has a long-standing interest in making technology accessible to women, people with limited literacy skills, and other underserved populations. She is now channeling that same urge to translate and illuminate in service of the humane treatment of dogs and joyful companionship between dogs and people. Her goal is to make training accessible and learning theory comprehensible to pet owners.

She holds bachelor's and master's degrees in music performance and a master's degree in engineering science. She received a Certificate of Excellence for completion of Susan Friedman's applied behavior analysis course for animal professionals, Living and Learning with Animals, in 2012. She lives in the mid-Southern U.S. and works at a nonprofit agency that helps impoverished women access medical care.

A Note from the Author

Thank you for reading my book. I hope it was helpful to you. If you'd like to read more of my writing, you can find me online at eileenanddogs.com (my behavior blog) and dogdementia.com (the website companion to this book).

Please spread the word about dementia in dogs and what we can do to help them. If you'd like to share your thoughts about this book on Amazon, recommend it on Goodreads, post about it on Facebook or Twitter, or pin it on Pinterest, you can find the book's links on all those sites at dogdementia.com/linklist.

I also invite you to follow me on Pinterest. I gather up all my favorite stuff from a variety of sources and post it on my boards at pinterest.com/eileenanddogs. —Eileen Anderson

Made in the USA
Monee, IL
08 February 2024

53153329R00089